Dictionary of Telecommunications

Dictionary of Telecommunications

Ashish Mittal

AUTHORSPRESS

Worldwide Circulation through Authorspress Global Network
First Published 2007
by
Authorspress
E-35/103, Jawahar Park
Laxmi Nagar, Delhi-110 092
e-mail: authorspress@yahoo.com

Dictionary of Telecommunications
ISBN 978-81-7273-412-1

Printed in India at Virgo Press, Delhi.

Preface.

A major step in human civilisation has been the development of telecommunications, or long-distance communication. Enabling people to exchange thoughts, ideas and feelings through equipment as varied as the radio, telegraph, telephone, television and the internet, telecommunications have proved distances redundant when it comes to the basic need of human communication. Information in the form of voice, symbols, pictures, or data, or a combination of these, is easily transmitted across the world, allowing communication through electronic equipment as close to face-to-face communication as possible.

Today, telecommunications finds applications in an astounding variety of ways: for example, the transmission of newspaper pages from editorial offices to printing plants by means of fascimile, broadcasting of television and radio, etc. Contributing to the growth in telecommunications capacity have been remarkable advances in integrated circuits, computers and satellite technology.

This book in the series of books designed for students pursing their Masters' in Education on comentrates its focus on presenting forth the readers an encyclopaedic dictionary of telecommunications terms. As technology crosses new frontiers, telecommunications is only set to better its creations and media. And with the pace of lifestyle also on a rapid increase, the further development of this field is a quarntee. The book makes conscientious effort to equip the readers with a guide which brings them upto-date and relevant information on telecommunications. Taking into account current trends, practice and developments in the field, the book attempts to delineate the terms in a lucid, comprehensive and insightful manner.

It is hoped that the book's content and insight makes it useful for the readers.

Ashish Mittal

A

Abbreviated Dialing: A feature that permits the calling party to dial the destination telephone number in fewer than normal digits. Abbreviated Dialing numbers must be set up in advance of their use. Speed Dialing is a typical example of Abbreviated Dialing.

Access: **(1)** Point at which entry is gained into a circuit or a network. May be switched or dedicated. **(2)** Ability to obtain data from a storage device or peripheral. **(3)** Type of connection between CPE and network.

Access Channels: Dedicated channels giving nondiscriminatory access to a local cable system by the public, government agencies or educational institutions.

Access Charge: A fee charged subscribers or other telephone companies by a local exchange carrier for the use of its local exchange networks.

Access Code: **(1)** Preliminary digits a user is required to dial to be connected to a particular trunk group, channel or line. **(2)** A short sequence of digits allowing a user to access a specific facility, service, feature or function of a telecommunications network or computer system .

Access Control: **(1)** Action taken to permit ordinary use of the components of a communications system. **(2)** The tasks performed by hardware, software and administrative controls to monitor system operation, ensure data integrity, perform user identification, record system access and changes and grant users access.

Access Gateway: Equipment used to provide the electronic "bridge" from the public switched telephone network (PSTN) to an Internet protocol (IP) network.

Access Line: A circuit between a subscriber and a switching center. Any line giving access to a larger system or network. Also, the private lines feeding a common control switching arrangement or enhanced private switched communications service switch from a PBX.

Access Method: **(1)** A technique for moving data, voice or video between main storage and input/output devices. **(2)** In local area networks, the technique and/or programme code used to determine use of the communications medium by granting access selectively to individual stations.

Access Point (AP): A base station in a wireless LAN. Access points are typically stand-alone devices that plug into an Ethernet hub or server. Like a cellular phone system, users can roam around with their mobile devices and be handed off from one access point to the other.

Access Services: Access services are specified sets of information transfer capabilities furnished to users at telecommunications network points-of-termination (POTs) to provide access to network transport services. Two examples are the following: subscriber access lines, the connection between a network POT (in this case more commonly known as a Network Interface NI) and a local exchange carrier switching system; and trunks between interexchange carrier points-of-presence and local exchange carrier switching systems (The POT at the POP is identified as the point of interface POI). End-to-end connections require originating and terminating access services.

Access Tandem: The switching system that provides distribution for originating or terminating traffic between End Offices and the Interexchange Carrier's Point-of-Termination. An Access Tandem is also used to distribute originating or terminating traffic between a CLEC end office and an intraLATA toll point or an Interexchange Carrier's Point of Termination

Account Codes: Also known as Project Codes or Bill-Back Codes. Account Codes are additional digits dialled by the calling party that provide information about the call. Typically used by hourly professionals (accountants, lawyers, etc.) to track and bill clients, projects, etc.

Account: Within billing terminology, this represents a customer's product or service location.

ACD: Automatic call distribution

Acknowledge Character (ack): Acknowledge character (ack) - A transmission control character transmitted as an affirmative response to a connecting station or to a sender.

Acoustic Echo Return Loss - AERL: The minimum loss experienced by a sound in travelling from the loudspeaker to the microphone in a conference room. It is expressed in dB or decibels. A 0 dB loss corresponds to a perfectly reflective room or to very close coupling between loudspeaker and microphone. In practice, AERL figures can range from 0 to -30 dB, with a poor room having the former figure.

Acoustic Echo Return Loss Enhancement - AERLE: The maximum echo cancellation provided by the acoustic canceller. Typical figures will vary from 6 to 18 dB. The larger the number the better. It is important to note whether the figure is quoted with the center clipper enabled or disabled. If quoted with center clipper disabled, it is a true measure of the cancellation provided by the echo canceller rather than the attenuation provided by the center clipper.

Acoustic Modem: A modulator-demodulator unit that converts data signals to telephone tones and back again.

Active Satellite: A satellite that transmits a signal, in contrast to a passive satellite that only reflects a signal. The signal received by the active satellite is usually amplified and translated to a different frequency before it is retransmitted. Ad Hoc: Teleconferencing technology and sites assembled for an event; equipment may be rented or permanently installed; sites are not always part of the network. Addressable: The ability to signal from the headend or hub site in such a way that only the desired subscriber's receiving equipment is affected. This makes it possible to send a signal to a subscriber and effect changes in the subscriber's level of service such as the ability to receive a programme.

Add/ Drop: The process where a part of the information carried in a transmission system is demultiplexed (dropped) at an intermediate point and different information is multiplexed (added) for subsequent transmission. The remaining traffic passes straight through the multiplexer without additional processing.

Add/Drop Multiplexer (ADM): A multiplexer capable of extracting and inserting lower-rate signals from a higher-rate multiplexed signal without completely demultiplexing the signal.

Address Signals: Address Signals convey destination information such as a called 4-digit extension number, central office code, and when required, area code and serving IXC carrier code. These signals may be generated by station equipment, or by a switching system.

ADPCM: Adaptive differential pulse code modulation: A method of compressing audio data by recording the differences between successive digital samples rather than full value of the samples. There are many different types of ADPCM standards; this refers to the standard as defined in the CD-ROM XA and CD-I standards.

ADPE (Automatic Data Processing Equipment): Deviceor interconnected system or subsystem used for the automatic acquisition, storage, manipulation, management, display, switching, transmission or reception of data or information.

ADSL: Asymmetric Digital Subscriber Line. A DSL, or Digital Subscriber Line, commonly transfers data to and from a subscribers premises by 'piggybacking' onto existing infrastructure, most commonly a standard analogue BT telephone line. Existing mains power supply cabling is sometimes utilised, also satellite or proprietary cabled networks. The data transfer is carried out by means of a high-frequency 'carrier' which does not interrupt the normal working of the existing service used as the vehicle for transmission. Data transfer is divided into two components - transmission and reception. In Asymmetric transfer (ADSL), one (usually transmission) is carried out at a slower rate than the other.

Advanced Television (ATV): New television technology that provides better audio and video quality than the current standard television broadcast system. High Definition TV (HDTV) is a form of ATV.

Affiliate Network: Group with their own satellite receive equipment; routinely receive same programming.

Affiliate: A broadcast station that airs a network's programmes and commercials, but is not owned by that network.

AFM: American Federation of Musicians. This union represents professional musicians in all areas of performance - recording and personal appearance.

AFTRA: American Federation of Television and Radio Artists. A union for artists who perform on broadcast media, including tape.

Agenda Item: At the FCC, a term that refers to the document which is to be voted on by the Commission at an agenda meeting. The final document is released to the public the same day or as soon as possible.

Agent: A person or organization that acts on behalf of another. In the telecommunications industry, Agents typically are independent individuals or companies that market the services of a carrier as if they were employees of that carrier.

Aggregator: An independent entity that brings several subscribers together to form a group that can obtain long-distance service at a reduced rate. Subscribers are billed by the original IXC. The aggregator only provides the initial set-up of the plan. He usually provides no service after that. Different than a reseller.

AIS (Alarm Indicating Signal): A code sent downstream indicating an upstream failure has occurred. SONET defines four categories of AIS: Line AIS, STS Path AIS, VT Path AIS, DSn AIS.

Alarm: A visual or audio signal which signifies that an error has occurred or an abnormal condition exists.

Algorithm: **1.** Rule of thumb for doing something with a semblance of intelligence. For example, a descrambling algorithm will yield a clear, unscrambled message from an apparently meaningless one. **2.** The procedure used for performing a task. America Online - AOL: Commercial information service with a graphical interface.

ALI Automatic Location Identification: A display of the caller's address, type of service and if a business - the name of the business, if a residence - the listed name associated with the displayed telephone number. The PSAP will also get a display of the associated emergency service number (ESN) information (police, fire, and ambulance).

All Trunks Busy (ATB): A single tone interrupted at a 120 impulses per minute (ipm) rate to indicate all lines or trunks in a routing group are busy.

Allocate: To assign a resource for use in performing a specific task.

Alpha Test: The stage during the research and development of a new product during which a prototype of the system is operated to determine whether the system concept and design are functional. Stage to identify areas that need further development and/or enhancement.

Alpha-geometric: A high resolution videotex display technique. Pictures are created by instructions such as draw a line, draw a circle, fill in an area. Picture definition is dependent upon the resolution capability of the display terminal.

Alpha-mosaic: A low resolution block-oriented videotex display technique. Picture definition is fixed at 64 by 60 elements, or pixels, no matter what the resolution capability of the display terminal.

Alternate Access: A form of local access where the provider is not the LEC, but is authorized or permitted to provide such service.

Alternate Access Carriers: Local exchange carriers in direct competition with the RBOCs. Normally found only in the larger metropolitan areas.

AlternateOperator Service Provider; AOS provider: A party, other than telephone companies, which provides operator services for long distance calls.

Alternate Provider of Long Distance Services: A company, other than a telephone company, that provides telecommunications services between exchanges that are not in the same toll-free calling area.

Alternate Route: A secondary communications path used to reach a destination if the primary path is unavailable.

Alternate Voice Data (AVD): A single transmission facility which can be used for either voice or data.

Alternative Operator Services: Operator services provided by a company other than a LECRBOC or AT&T that is authorized to provide such service.

Amateur Radio Operator : A noncommercial, private radio operator. There are six classes of amateur radio licenses that can be earned after passing FCC-administered examinations.

American Standard Code for Information Interchange (ACSII): American Standard Code for Information Interchange (ACSII) - A code with seven information signals plus one parity check signal, designed for interworking between computers (i.e., the transmittal of text). The most popular coding method used by computers for converting letters, numbers, punctuation and control codes with digital form.

AMI: Alternate Mark Inversion. The line-coding format in transmission systems where successive ones (marks) are alternatively inverted (sent with polarity opposite that of the preceding mark).

Amplifier: A device used to increase the strength of video and audio electronic signals. Amplitude: The size or magnitude of a voltage or current waveform; the strength of a signal.

Amplitude Modulation (AM): A type of transmission used in either the standard radio broadcast band at 535-1705 kilohertz, shortwave broadcasting, and in some private radio services such as citizens band (CB) and aviation.

AMPS (Advanced Mobile Phone System): The most common type of analog cellular telephone system in the United States, operating at 800 MHz to 900 MHz. Most of these first-generation (1G) systems have been or are being replaced by second-generation (2G) digital networks.

Analog: A transmission method employing a continuous (rather than pulsed or digital) electrical signal that varies in amplitude or frequency in response to changes of sound, light, position, etc., imposed on a transducer in the sending device; opposite of digital.

Analog Carrier System: An analog carrier system is a transmission system that uses repeaters that compensate for analog medium impairments, and produce output signals that are linear-scaled versions of input signals. Analog carrier systems can carry speech, data, video and supervisory signals although they are best suited for speech signals.

Analog Signal: An analog signal is a continuous electrical signal that varies in direct correlation with an impressed phenomenon, stimulus, or event that bears intelligence. Sound waves and their electrical analogs are characterized by loudness (amplitude) and pitch. Analog signals can assume any of an infinite number of amplitude values or states within a specified range, in accordance with or analogous to, an impressed stimulus. Pitch refers to how many times per second the signal swings between high and low amplitudes, i.e., its frequency.

Analog-to-Digital - A/D Conversion: The conversion of an analog signal into a digital equivalent. An A/D converter samples or measures an input voltage and outputs a digitally encoded number corresponding to that voltage. Analog Transmission: Transmission of a continuously variable signal as opposed to a discrete signal. Physical quantities such as temperature are described as analog while data characters are coded in discrete pulses and are referred to as digital. Animate: To effect motion of any sort; e.g. to animate a person's presentation. Animation: A video, film, and computer production technique utilizing cartoon-type artwork to create the illusion of movement.

Analogue: Analogue refers to signals that can represent an infinite range of numbers, as opposed to digital which can only be distinct whole numbers. Analogue data often comes from measurements, like a sine wave. The sound a modem makes over the phone is analog since it can be any of a number of different frequencies. The fixed-line networks usually transfer analogue data and fax.

Analogue transmission; analog transmission: In telephony, a method of conveying voice, data, image or video information by a signal that varies continuously in amplitude or frequency with the information being transmitted.

ANI: Automatic Number Identification: 1. A service feature in which the directory number or equipment number of a calling station is automatically obtained. Note: ANI is used in message accounting. **2.** The code that provides the billing number of the line or trunk that originated a call. **3.** A system that identifies the billing account for a call. For 911 systems, the ANI identifies the calling party and may be used as a call back number.

Ani failure: Failure of the end central office to identify the call and provide the automatic number identification to the tandem office; or, an ANI failure between the tandem office and the PSAP. Without ANI, the call cannot be properly routed or provide an ALI display.

Annoying call; offensive call: An unwanted or disturbing (i.e., obscene, threatening) telephone call.

Anonymous call: If a caller misdials and dials the seven-digit number associated with the PSAP trunk group, the call will come in on a 9-1-1 trunk. The ANI display will display an anonymous call. The seven-digit numbers associated with the PSAP positions are not published, even to the PSAPs.

ANSI: American National Standards Institute. A membership organization founded in 1918 that coordinates the development of U.S. voluntary national standards in both the private and public sectors. It is the U.S. member body to ISO and IEC. Information technology standards pertain to programming languages, EDI, telecommunications and physical properties of diskettes, cartridges and magnetic tapes.

Answer Supervision: (1) An off-hook signal indicating when the called party answers; used to read calls for billing purposes. **(2)** A signal generated by the originating switch (hardware answer supervision) or by the switch which terminates the call (software answer supervision, when FGA or WATS is used to terminate the call).

Answerback: A signal sent by a data receiver to a data transmitter indicating it is ready to receive data, or is acknowledging the receipt of data.

Antenna Power: The product of the square of the broadcast antenna current and the antenna resistance where the current is measured.

Application Layer: The top layer of the OSI seven-layer logical structure for data services; the end-user layer.

Application: The use of a technology to achieve a specific objective. Application Software: In computers, programmes used to interact with and accomplish work for the user. Application software is usually written in a higher computer language such as Basic, COBOL, FORTRAN or Pascal, and may be written by the user or supplied by the manufacturer or a software company.

Applications Programme: A computer programme dedicated to a specific purpose or task. Applications programmes which produce discernible results and can sometimes be machine-independent, are distinct from systems programmes, which are designed to drive particular electronic devices and are always machine-dependent. Archie: A system which allows searching of indexes of files available on public servers on the Internet.

Applications Software: The instructions that direct the hardware to perform specific functions. Common software applications include payroll, inventory control and electronic spreadsheets.

Architecture: How system components are designed, connected to and operate with one another. Architecture determines the ability of a network to manage voice, video, data and text. Descriptions of architecture include the ability of the system to carry narrow, medium and broadband signals.

Archival: A medium that is readable and/or writable for an extended period. Armored Cable: Coaxial cable that can be direct buried without protective conduit, or used in underwater applications.

Archive: A procedure for transferring information from an on-line storage diskette or memory area to an off-line storage medium.

Area code: The three-digit numbering plan area code in North America which permits direct distance dialing on the telephone system.

ARPANet: A predecessor of the Internet. Started in 1969 with funds from the Defence Department's Advanced Research Projects Agency.

Artificial Intelligence: The capability of a computer to perform functions that are normally associated with human intelligence, such as reasoning, learning or self-improvement.

ASCII (American Standard Code for Information Interchange): The American Standard Code for Information Interchange (ASCII) is an 8-level code accepted worldwide as a communication standard to achieve compatibility between data services.

ASP (Application Service Provider): Third parties that manage and distribute software services to customers from a central data facility. Clients "rent" instead of buy applications for many back-office and e-commerce applications, including e-commerce, messaging and other Web hosting services.

Aspect Ratio: The ratio of picture width to height (4 to 3 for North American NTSC broadcast video).

Assembler: (1) A programme capable of translating assembly code into digit code. The first major step in the automation of software development. Permitting symbolic (i.e., named) references to storage locations, rather than requiring the use of numbers, and eliminating the necessity to programme in binary or other machine language.

Assembly Code: Programming language with statements that may be instructions or declarations. The instructions usually have a one-to-one correspondence with machine instructions.

Assign: To give a new value to a variable during the running of a programme.

Asterisk Laws: Gives consumers the right to say they don't want to receive marketing phone calls by choosing to have an asterisk next to their names in the telephone book. The asterisk means "no phone solicitations."

Asynchronous Communication: Takes place in different time frames and accessed at the user's convenience. Synchronous communication takes place in the same time frame such as a live teleconference.

Asynchronous Computer: A computer in which each operation starts as a result of a signal generated by the completion of the previous operation, or by the availability of the parts of the computer required by the next event or operation.

Asynchronous Time-Division Multiplexing: An asynchronous signal transmission mode that makes use of time-division multiplexing.

Asynchronous Transfer Mode (ATM): A multiplexing/switching technique in which information is organized into fixed-length cells with each cell consisting of an identification header field and an information field. The transfer mode is asynchronous in the sense that the use of the cells depends on the required or instantaneous bit rate.

Asynchronous Transmission: Transmission method in which the intervals between transmitted characters may be unequal of length. Transmission is controlled by start and stop bits at the beginning and end of each character. This way, if there is line noise, the modem can find out right away where the next byte should start.

Asynchronous: A transmission method in which information is transferred one discrete character at a time and is delineated by a start and stop indicator at the beginning and end of the character. The opposite of asynchronous is SYNCHRONOUS transmission.

ATM (Asynchronous Transfer Mode): High bandwidth communications transmission technology that enables the high-speed transmission of data, including voice, multimedia, full-motion video and videoconferencing. ATM currently supports transmission speeds from 64 kbps to 622 mbps.

Attention characters: The letters "AT", which get the modem's attention that you are about to send it a command.

Attenuation Coefficient: Rate of optical power loss with respect to distance along the fiber, measured in decibels per kilometer (dB/km) at a specific wavelength. The lower the number, the better the fiber's attenuation characteristics. Typical multimode wavelengths are 850 and 1300 nanometers (nm); single mode wavelengths are 1310 and 1550 nm.

Attenuation: Reduction in power level due to line resistance, leakage or induction which results in the received signal being lower in volume than the original transmitted signal. [In optical fiber systems there are other causes of attenuation, such as absorption, scattering and losses into radiation modes. It is usually expressed in decibel (dB).]

ATU-C (ADSL Transmission Unit-Central Office): Device at the Central Office end of an ADSL, between the line and the telephone switch, that supports high-speed data transmission in conjunction with an ATU-R at the customer's premises.

ATU-R (ADSL Transmission Unit-Remote): Device at the downstream end of an ADSL, between the line and the subscriber's equipment, that supports high-speed data transmission in conjunction with a ATU-C at the Central Office.

Audible Ringing Tone: The information tone sent back to the calling party to indicate the called line is being rung.

Audio Bridge: An audio bridge connects the telephones at remote sites, equalizes the noise distortion and background noise for a live audio teleconference. Audio Frequency: A frequency lying within the audible spectrum (the band of frequencies extending from about 20 Hz to 20 kHz).

Audio Presentation: Often overlooked, but just as important as the video (perhaps more so) is the sound portion of the programme. Without the audio, nothing is understood while a video failure could be tolerated if the sound portion is not affected. Use a good audio system to augment the video display. Do not use the built-in speaker of the TV monitor or room PA system. Rather, employ a high quality stand-alone system, with the speakers positioned adjacent to the TV screen. This affords the best audio experience. The audio quality coming off the satellite signal is true high fidelity, and its reproduction further enhances programme presentation.

Audio Response Unit: Device that provides a spoken response to digital inquiries from a telephone or other device. The response is composed from a prerecorded vocabulary of words and can be transmitted over telecommunication lines to the location from which the inquiry originated.

Audio Teleconferencing: Two-way electronic voice communication between two or more groups, or three or more individuals, who are in separate locations. Audiographic: Teleconference system which uses narrow band telecommunications channels (telephone lines or subcarriers); transmits audio and graphics. Graphics can be transmitted by facsimile transceivers (transmitter-receiver), computers (text or graphic display).

Audio Text: The term used to describe a system that provides automated interactive telephone information, such as stock prices, sports scores and personals.

Audio-Subcarrier: Frequency which transmits audio for an accompanying video signal or independent audio (such as a radio programme). Audio is sent along with the video signal, but on a different frequency.

Aural Cable: Services providing FM-only original programming to cable systems on a lease basis.

Authentication: Process of verifying with certainty the identity of a valid subscriber or ITSP through the use of a unique user identification number, password or other method (i.e., verifying that customers are who they say they are).

Authoring System: Computer software that allows one to develop the framework for an interactive multimedia presentation. Authoring software enables the use of multiple data types as well as the controls needed to play-back information on the computer from devices such as CD-ROMs, computer hard disks and videodiscs. Automatic Number Identification - ANI: The automatic identification of a calling station, usually for automatic message accounting. Also used in pay-per-view automated telephone order entry to identify a customer for billing and programme authorization purposes.

Authorization Code: **(1)** Code that identifies the customer, and is used for billing purposes and validation by the switch. **(2)** An identification number that the customer enters when placing a call.

Authorization Process: Before an alternate long distance company can approach Bell Canada Carrier Services to implement a change to a customer's long distance service, it must obtain appropriate authorization from the customer. That authorization can take one of three forms: verbal, written or electronic.

Auto Reliable: The ability of a modem to be able to communicate both with modems that do have error-control and/or data compression, and those that do not.

Auto-delivery: A feature of a computer-based message system in which messages are delivered automatically to terminals equipped to answer incoming calls. bv0

Auto-dial: Automatic dialing; the capability of a terminal, modem, computer or a similar device to place a call and establish a connection over the switched telephone network without operator intervention.

Automatic Call Distribution (ACD): ACD is a means for efficiently directing and managing large numbers of incoming calls to specific departments/terminals within an organization.

Automatic Callback: A feature of a communications device or network that records, and can dial, the originating phone number of the last incoming call.

Automatic calling unit (ACU): A device which, on receipt of information from a computer, automatically dials calls over the communications network.

Automatic Dialing Device (ADD): Automatic equipment, which has the capability to store telephone numbers to be called, used for telephone solicitation with live voice callers.

Automatic Dialing Unit: A device which automatically generates a predetermined set of dialing digits when the corresponding button is pushed.

Automatic Dialing-announcing Device (ADAD): Automatic equipment used for telephone solicitation which has the capability to store telephone numbers, which can be used alone, or in conjunction with other equipment, to convey a prerecorded or synthesized voice message.

Automatic Message Accounting (AMA): A system which automatically collects the accounting information required to bill long distance calls.

Automatic Message-Switching Center: In a communications network, location at which messages are automatically directed according to routing information within the message.

Automatic Protection Switching (APS): The ability of a network element to detect a failed working line and switch the service to a spare (protection) line. 1+1 APS pairs a protection line with each working line. 1:n APS provides one protection line for every n working lines.

Automatic route selection (ARS): Device (or software) which chooses the lowest cost ròute for long-distance calls over specific lines or services, including WATS, leased, specialized non-Bell common carriers (MCI, Sprint) or direct distance dialing (DDD).

Auxiliary Service Station: A type of station used by television and radio stations to facilitate the broadcast of programming to the general public.

Availability: **(1)** The degree to which a system or resource is operable and not in a state of congestion or failure at any given point in time. **(2)** The percentage of total trunks in a group which can be accessed by a particular switch.

AWG (American Wire Gauge): Measure of the thickness of copper telephone wire; the lower the number, the thicker the wire. Telephone wire varies from 18 to 26 AWG.

Azimuth: Angle between an antenna beam and the meridian plane, measured along a horizontal plane. How far east or west in the southerly sky the satellite is located in relation to the local meridian, or north-south plane. It is measured in degrees, clockwise from true north.

B

Backbone Network: A backbone network is a transmission facility designed to interconnect often lower-speed distribution networks, channels, or clusters of dispersed terminals or devices.

Backbone Wiring: In a premises distribution system, backbone wiring is the cable connecting telecommunications closets and equipment rooms within a building, and/or between buildings in a campus. Backbone wiring is sometimes referred to as the riser subsystem.

Backbone: The part of the communications network that carries the heaviest traffic. It joins the LAN via bridges and/or routers and serves as a communications highway for LAN to LAN traffic. It is also a basis of design for the overall network.

Background bit error ratio (BBER): (1) The ratio of the number of bits in error to the total number of bits received, exclusive of error bursts, over a special measurement period. **(2)** The error performance of the system under normal operation and does not include error bursts caused by line switching, maintenance, activity, etc.

Background errors: Errors that occur during the normal operation of the system. They generally occur one at a time or a few at a time.

Backhaul: A term used for the transmission of a signal (normally video) from the ends of transmission systems such as microwave to a central point. For a satellite videoconference, a backhaul refers to a signal brought in from a secondary site to the origination site, mixed with the primary signal, and sent out over the programme out satellites.

Backup: The provision, logical or physical, of facilities to speed the process of restart and recovery following failure. Facilities may include duplicated files of transactions, periodic dumping of core or backing storage contents, duplicated processors, storage devices, terminals, telecommunications hardware or the switches to effect a changeover.

Ballot: A release form that authorizes a customer's long-distance phone service to be switched to (another) long-distance carrier, or reseller. Also know as a Letter Of Agency or LOA.

Balloting: Balloting is a process, not unlike a political referendum, by which all residence and business customers would be asked to "vote" for a preferred or primary (1+) long distance provider.

Balun: Balanced/unbalanced. A device which connects a balanced (two-wire) line, such as a phone line, to an unbalanced (coaxial) line, like cable. The two-wire line is called balanced because the currents in each wire are equal and in opposite directions.

BAN - Billing Account Number: Used by telephone companies to designate a billing account, i.e., a customer or customer location that receives a bill. A customer may have any number of BANs.

Band; Frequency Band: A contraction of the term frequency band. A range of frequencies between two defined limits (e.g., the voiceband in telephony is approximately 300 to 3,000 hertz).

Banded Rates: Tariffed rates which may be changed by the carrier within a specified range. Frequently, state commissions require notice to the commission prior to each change. Banded rates are being used less frequently today.

Bar-code Scanner: (1) Optical character reader. A device used to read bar-codes by means of reflected light, such as the scanners that read the Universal Product Codes on supermarket products.

Base Band Distribution Systems: Usually used when the viewing areas are close together, and when TV monitors are used for viewing. The base band audio/video output from the satellite receivers is fed directly into the monitor. This form of wiring uses several twisted pair wires which can be very expensive when wiring more than 50 feet because of the need for many amplifiers and splitters. The picture quality is much sharper using a base band system, than with any other system.

Base Station: A land station in the land mobile service. For example, in cellular and personal communications uses, each cell has its own base station; each base station is interconnected with other base stations and with the public switched network.

Basic Rate Interface - BRI: The basic subscriber loop for one or two users, which delivers two 64 kpbs B channels and one 16 kbps D channel over a standard twisted pair loop. Each circuit-switched B channel can transmit voice or data simultaneously. The D channel transmits call control messages and user packet data.

Basic Service: Minimum set of capabilities deemed necessary for use of the public telecommunications network. Current basic service includes an access line, with access to local and long distance calling, to emergency calling (911), and to voice/nonvoice relay service.

Basic Telephone Service: In the context of the objective of affordable, universal telephone service, basic service refers to residential telephone service provided to the general body of customers. Examples of current basic service features include: the provision of dial tone; access to operator assistance; a personal listing in the telephone directory; repair service; and long distance calling.

Basic Trading Area (BTA): Geographic boundaries that segment the country for licensing purposes. BTAs are based on Rand McNally's Commercial Atlas & Marketing Guide. BTA boundaries follow county lines and include the county or counties whose residents make the bulk of their shopping goods purchases in the area. The FCC has used BTAs to license number of services including broadband and narrowband Personal Communication Services.

BASIC: Beginners All-purpose Symbolic Instruction Code. It is a programming language. It is called symbolic because it allows programmers to use symbols to represent numbers and information.

Batched Communication: The sending of a large body of data from one station to another station network, without intervening responses from the receiving unit.

Baud Rate: A measure of signalling speed in data communications that specifies the maximum number of signal elements transmitted each second.

Baud: A term referring to the speed at which modems communicate. Technically, it is the number of changes in an electronic signal per second. Since the number of changes used to be the same as the number of bits sent or received per second, bps and baud are often used interchangeably. However, there is a difference, which is very often confused.

Baudot: mA seven bit code, only five of which are information bits. Baudot is used by some text telephones to communicate with each other.

BBS - Bulletin Board System/Service: The BBS is an area within a network where users can "post" information for public display, in much the same way one posts information on a regular bulletin board. Most networks dedicate a bulletin board to special interest areas, such as education or computer care.

BCE Inc.: BCE Inc. is Canada's largest telecommunications company. Its subsidiaries include: Bell Canada, Canada's largest telecommunications services supplier; Northern Telecom Limited, an equipment manufacturer; Bell-Northern Research Ltd., a research and development establishment; BCE Mobile Communications Inc., a cellular/paging/mobile data company; and Tele-Direct Publications Inc ., a telephone directory publisher. Another subsidiary, Bell Canada International Inc., makes investments in telecommunications companies internationally. BCE has more registered shareholders than any other Canadian company.

Bell Canada International Inc. (BCI): BCI seeks investments in international telecommunications markets that provide a synergy with BCE's other telecommunications activities. BCI administers investments in telecommunications services, cable television/telephone and cellular services in the United Kingdom, the United States, New Zealand and Colombia.

Bell Canada: Canada's largest supplier of telecommunications services. It provides advanced voice, data and image communications to approximately nine million customers in Ontario and Québec. Bell is federally regulated by the Canadian Radio-television and Telecommunications Commission (CRTC) and is a member of Stentor - an alliance of Canada's major telephone companies.

Bell Customer Code: A three-digit numeric code, appended to the end of the Main Billing Telephone Number, that is used by Local Exchange Carriers to provide unique identification of customers.

Bell Mobility: BCE Mobile Communications Inc., operating under the Bell Mobility banner, is the Canadian leader in mobile communications. BCE Mobile is more than 65 per cent owned by BCE.

Bell Operating Company: Local telephone company formerly owned by AT&T. These companies, such as Southwestern Bell and Ameritech, were formed by the breakup of the AT&T system on January 1, 1984. Also known as Regional Bell Operating Companies or Baby Bells.

Bell System: Prior to Jan. 1, 1984, an aggregate term for AT&T encompassing 24 Bell operating companies providing local exchange phone service, the AT&T Long Lines Division providing long distance connections, an equipment manufacturing arm known as Western Electric, and a research and development arm known as Bell Laboratories. The Bell System was broken up by the AT&T divestiture.: BOC: Bell Operating Company. The local Bell operating company. Currently there are 22 BOCs organized into seven Regional Bell Operating Companies, also known as RBOCs.

Bell-Northern Research Ltd. (BNR): Bell-Northern Research is a world leader in the design and development of advanced telecommunications systems. BNR operates or supports laboratories in Canada, the United Kingdom, the United States, Australia, Japan and China.

Bent Pipe Technology: Technology for transmitting calls from one point on Earth to an orbiting satellite and back down to another point on Earth.

BETA test: The stage at which a new product is tested under actual usage conditions. The purpose of beta testing is to locate and correct potential problems before consumer marketing begins. Follows Alpha Testing.

Beyond the Horizon Region: That physical region beyond the optical horizon with which line-of- sight radio communications is not normally possible, but can occur if atmospheric conditions are such to cause beam bending or forward scattering of the radio signal.

Bicycle Tapes: The process whereby video tape material is distributed by sending or "bicycling" the tape after presentation to the next site for its scheduled presentation.

Bid: (1) An attempt to gain control over a line in order to transmit data. (2) Usually associated with contention style of sharing a single line among several terminals. [Non-uniform time-outs at each terminal for reinstituting a bid if the line is busy give assurance that each terminal can have access to the line.

Bidding Credit: A spectrum auction term. It is a credit given to eligible FCC auction applicants which allows them to receive a discount on their winning bids in an auction.

Bidirectional Flow: A pathway allocating two-way data or communication exchange; flow in either direction represented on the same flow line in a flowchart. Binary: Numbering system with two possible states, on or off as designated by 0 and 1.

Bidirectional: Operating in both directions. Bidirectional APS allows protection switching to be initiated by either end of the line.

Billed Telephone Number (BTN): The "main number" of a customer's service that the LEC uses as a customer's account number. It is usually also an actual ANI. Will generally have WTNs associated with it. Every separate, distinct phone bill a customer gets will generally have a separate BTN.

Billing Account Number - BAN: Used by telephone companies to designate a customer or customer location that will be billed. A single customer may have multiple billing accounts.

Billing Cycle: A recurring period of time between traffic cut-off dates which precedes customer billing. Cycles are typically 30 days.

Bill-to-Room: A billing option associated with Operator Assisted calls that allows the calling party to bill a call to their hotel room. With this option, the carrier is required to notify the hotel, upon completion of the call, of the time and charges.

Binary: A number system based upon twos rather than tens and that uses only two characters, zero (0) and one (1).

Binary Digit: Unit of information in two-level digital notation which may be 0 or 1. A member selected from a binary set.

Binary Information Unit or Binary Digit (BIT): The smallest unit of digital information. A single digit number in "base-2", either a 0 or a 10. Bandwidth is usually measured in bits-per-second (bps).

Binary N-Zero Suppression (BNZS): Line coding system that replaces N number of zeros with a special code to maintain pulse density required for synchronization. N is typically 3, 6, or 8. BIP-8 (Bit Interleaved Parity-8) A method of error checking in SONET which allows a full set of performance statistics to be generated. For example, a BIP-8 creates eight-bit (one-byte) groups, then does a parity check for each of the eight bit positions in the byte.

Binary Synchronous Transmission (BSC or bisync): (1) Data transmission in which synchronization of characters is controlled by timing signals generated at the sending and receiving stations. **(2)** A half-duplex, character-oriented data communications protocol. Contrast with asynchronous transmission.

Binding Post: A binding post is a screw with a small nut mounted on a terminal box. Wires are joined together by wrapping them around a screw and then tightening the nut on them.

Bipolar Signals: Bipolar signals are signals in which positive and negative pulses, always alternating, represent one binary signal state only. The absence of pulses represents the other binary state.

Bird: A colloquial expression used to refer to a communications satellite.

Bit-Interleaved Parity (BIP): A parity check that groups all the bits in a block into units (such as byte), then performs a parity check for each bit position in a group.

Bit Density: A measure of the number of bits received per unit of length or area.

Bit Duration: **(1)** Equivalent to the time that it takes one encoded bit to pass a point on the transmission medium. **(2)** In serial communications, a relative unit of time measurement used for comparison of delay times where the data rate of a transmission channel can vary (for example propagation delay, access latency).

Bit Error Rate (BER): BER is the ratio of the number of bits received with errors to the total number of bits transmitted. BER and the average number of error-free seconds are the principal impairment measurements for digital channels.

Bit Map: A matrix of dots, all of the same density, that form an image.

Bit Rate: Bit rate is the capacity characteristic of digital signals as defined by the number of bits (or bytes) per second that a channel will support. For example, a transmission facility that can support information exchange at the rate of I megabit per second (1 Mbps or 1,000,000 bits per second) delivers the same quantity of information, i.e., throughput, as a 1 kilobit per second (kbps or 1,000 bits per second) facility, but, in only 1/1000 of the time.

Bit Stream: A continuous string of bit positions occurring serially in time.

Bit Stuffing: In asynchronous systems, a technique used to synchronize asynchronous signals to a common rate before multiplexing.

Bit Synchronous: A way of mapping payload into virtual tributaries that synchronizes all inputs into the VTs, but does not capture any framing information or allow access to subrate channels carried in each input. For example, bit synchronous mapping of a channeled DS1 into a VT1.5 does not provide access to the DS0 channels carried by the DS1.

Bit Transfer Rate: The number of bits transferred per unit time, usually expressed in bits per second (bps).

BITNET: Another, academically oriented, international computer network, which uses a different set of computer instructions to move data. It is easily accessible to Internet users through e-mail, and provides a large number of conferences and databases. Its name comes from "Because It's Time." BITNET is linked to Net North, the Canadian equivalent, and EARN, the European Academic and Research Network, as well as Internet/NREN.

Bit-oriented: Describes a communications protocol or transmission procedure where control information is encoded in fields of one or more bits; oriented toward full-duplex link operation.

Bits Per Second (bps): The number of bits passing a point every second. The transmission rate for digital information.

Black box: A generic term used to identify functional equipment segments, as opposed to circuitry, that make up each segment of a telecommunications system.

Blackout: A term used to describe the non-broadcast of a live event (i.e. sports, cultural) usually imposed by the sponsor(s) of the event.

Blanking (picture): The portion of the composite video signal whose instantaneous amplitude makes the vertical and horizontal retrace invisible. Blanking Level: The level of the front and back porches of the composite video signal.

Blanking Pulse: 1. A signal used to cut off the electron beam and thus remove the spot of light on the face of a television picture tube or image tube. **2.** A signal used to suppress the picture signal at a given time for a required period.

Block Calls: Prevent calls from completing to the requested destination. May be due to network problems (outage, overload, etc.), or by customer request (e.g. block calls from-or-to certain NPAs, NXXs, States, LATAs, etc.).

Block Error Rate (BLER): One of the underlying concepts of error performance is the notion of Errored Blocks, that is, blocks in which one or more bits are in error. A block is a set of consecutive bits associated with the path or section monitored by means of an Error Detection Code (EDC), such as Bit Interleaved Parity (BIP). Block Error rate (BLER) is calculated with the formula: BLER = errored blocks received/ total blocks sent Bit Error vs. Block Error Error rate statistics play a key role in measuring the performance of a network.

As errors increase, user payload (especially data) must be re-transmitted. The end effect is creation of more (nonrevenue) traffic in the network.

Block Error Rate Test (BLERT): (1) In data communications testing, the ratio between the total number of blocks transmitted in a given message and the number of blocks in that message received in error. **(2)** A measure of the quality of a data transmission.

Block Length: A measure of the size of a block, usually specified in units such as records, words, computer words or characters.

Block Size: When used with either error control or data compression protocols, refers to the number of characters to be sent at one time. If error control is used, the codes are sent immediately following this block. Typical block sizes are 64, 128, 192, or 256 characters. Small block sizes are better when the line quality is bad (such as for long distance calls), while large block sizes are better during good connections (such as for local calls).

Block: A string of records, words or characters treated as a logical entity. Blocks are separated by interblock gaps, and each block may contain one or more records.

Blocked Calls: All attempted calls that are not connected. Two most common reasons for non-connections: all lines to the central offices are in use; all connecting paths through the PBX/switch are in use.

Blockwiring: The cabling and termination equipment installed between TJF and Distribution Cases on floors or in risers. Some users with Bluetooth may try to send text messages to strangers without saying who they are (nicknamed 'bluejacking'). To prevent 'bluejacking' make sure your phone is not visible to other mobile phones.

Bluetooth: A new technology designed to be embedded in electronic devices in order to provide wireless and seamless connections over short distances. The idea is to provide an easier to use alternative to the cable-based interfaces currently in use to link computers and computer peripherals. Other devices in which Bluetooth chips could be embedded include mobile telephones, personal digital assistants, headsets and wristwatches.

B-Mac: A method of transmitting and scrambling television signals where MAC (multiplexed analog component) signals are time-multiplexed with a digital burst containing digitized sound, video synchronizing, authorization, and information.

BMI and ASCAP: Broadcast Music Incorporated and American Society Composers and Publishers which serve the same function of licensing and collecting creative royalties on works of music played in live public performance and recordings.

BOC (Bell-operating Company): BOC is the common term for one of 24 local exchange carrier telephone companies that were part of the Bell System prior to divestiture. All but two of the BOCs (Southern New England Telephone in Connecticut and Cincinnati Bell in Ohio) are owned and managed by one of 7 regional Bell holding companies (RBHCs).

Booster: A television or FM broadcast station, operating at relatively low power that receives a distant input signal, amplifies it, and retransmits it on the same channel.

Booting: Technique for loading a programme into a computer's memory in which the programme's initial instructions direct the loading of the rest of the programme. Usually, a few manual instructions must be entered on a keyboard, or a switch implemented to initiate the process.

Bootstrap Loader: An input routine in which simple preset computer operations are used to load instructions that in turn cause further instructions to be loaded until the complete computer programme is in storage.

Bounce: What your e-mail does when it cannot get to its recipient - it bounces back to you - unless it goes off into the ether, never to be found again.

Branching: A computer operation, such as switching, where a choice is made between two or more possible courses of action depending upon some related fact or condition.

Break: **(1)** To interrupt the sending of a message and take control of the circuit at the receiving end. **(2)** An interruption in continuity.

Breakout Box: A device that allows access to individual points on a physical interface connector for testing and monitoring.

Breakout Panel: A breakout box mounted as a component in some larger device.

Bridge Tap: Bridge tap is an undetermined length of wire attached between the normal endpoints of a circuit that introduces unwanted impedance imbalances for data transmission.

Bridge: Device which interconnects three or more telecommunication channels, such as telephone lines. A telephone conference audio bridge links three or more telephones (usually operated assisted). Usually a meet-me audio bridge or provides a teleconference direct dial access number. Both connect remote sites and equalize noise distortion.

Bridges, Gateway, Routers: Devices that convert LANs to other LANs, computers and WANs by allowing systems running on different media (copper wire, fiber optics, etc.) and protocols (rules to communicate).

Broadband Network: A local area network (LAN) residing on coaxial cable capable of transporting multiple data, voice and video channels.

Broadcasting: The dissemination of any form of radio electric communications by means of Hertzian waves intended to be received by the public. Transmission through space, utilizing preassigned radio frequencies, which are capable of being received aurally or visually by an audience. The one-way transmission of information.

Brokers: Organizations which maintain primary leases or ownership of communications satellite time and provide subleases to teleconference originators.

Browser: A software programme used to query, search and view information on computer sites connected to the Internet.

BSI: British Standards Institute, who are responsible for the drawing up of standards against which equipment is designed for sale in the UK.

BTN - Billing Telephone Number: The phone number associated, for billing purposes, with the Working Phone Number.

Buffer Box: A device that temporarily stores data, usually between two devices with different data speeds; sends data out at a speed that the slower machine can handle. Recommended to prevent CDR loss on a call accounting system.

Buffer: Temporary storage facility used as an interface between system elements whose data rates are different; Memory area in computer or peripheral device used for temporary storage of information that has just been received. The information is held in the buffer until the computer or device is ready to process it. Hence, a computer or device with memory designated as a buffer area can process one set of data while more sets are arriving.

Bulletin Board: An electronic message center accessible through computer-aided communication lines.

Bundle: A package that includes several products for one price. For example, a CDROM drive, with controller card, cable, software, and one or more CD-ROMs. Bus Interface: An electronic pathway between CPUs and input/output devices. A bus interface for a CD-ROM drive consists of a controller card and cable.

Burst errors: Bits or signals lost due to such problems as line switching or multiplex switching.

Burst Modem: In satellite communications, an electronic device used at each station that sends high-speed bursts of data which are interleaved with one another. These bursts must be precisely timed to avoid data collisions with multiple stations.

Burst Transmission: Data transmission at a specific data signalling rate during controlled intermittent fiintervals.

Burst: **1.** In data communication, a sequence of signals counted as one unit in accordance with some specific criterion or measure. **2.** A colour burst.

Bus: **(1)** A heavy conductor, or group of conductors, to which several units of the same type of equipment may be connected. **(2)** A path or channel for transmitting electrical signals and data, usually between a computer and peripheral equipment.

Business Applications: Business applications are unique aggregations of telecommunications services that satisfy particular enterprise needs.

Business Exchange Measured Service (BEMS): A usage-sensitive rating structure for business local service in which business customers pay a reduced flat rate for access to the telephone network and a separate per-minute charge for their outgoing local calling. Incoming calls, long distance calls, operator-handled and directory assistance calls, and local calls internal to a business's own system are excluded.

Business Television - BTV: Corporate use of video transmission for meetings/training via satellite.

Busy: Call condition in which transmission facilities are already in use.

Busy hour calls: The number of calls anticipated during each Public Safety Answering Point's busiest period.

Busy hour: **(1)** The peak 60 minutes during a business day when the largest volume of communications traffic is handled. **(2)** When phone lines are most in demand and/or most used.

Busy tone: A single tone that is interrupted at 60 ipm (impulses per minute) rate to indicate that the call's terminating location is already in use.

Bypass: The routing of calls through networks other than the public switched telephone network in order to avoid the fees which subsidize local rates.

Byte Interleaved: Bytes from each STS-1 are placed in sequence in a multiplexed or concatenated STS-N signal. For example, for an STS-3, the sequence of bytes from contributing STS-1s is 1,2,3,1,2,3, ...

Byte Synchronous: A way of mapping payload into virtual tributaries that synchronizes all inputs into the VTs, captures framing information, and allows access to subrate channels carried in each input.

Byte: **(1)** The representation of a character. **(2)** A group of eight bits makes a byte. Typically a 16-bit "word" is itself divided into two bytes for handling. **(3)** Unit of measurement used to rate storage capacity of disks; usually the smallest addressable unit of information in a data store or memory. One thousand bytes is a kilobyte; one million bytes is a megabyte.

C

C Band: A portion of the electromagnetic spectrum used heavily for satellite and microwave transmission; frequencies of approximately 4 to 6 GHz.

C/N - C/NR - Carrier to Noise Ratio: Refers to the ratio of the satellite carrier (or signal) to noise level in a given channel. Usually measured in dB at the LNA output.

Cable Communications Policy Act of 1984: This act, passed by Congress in 1984, updated the original Communications Act of 1934. The primary changes dealt with cable television regulation, theft of service, equal employment opportunity (EEO) an various licensing procedure changes.

Cable Compatible: Generally refers to consumer devices, such as television sets and videocassette recorders, that are designed and constructed to allow direct connection of a CATV subscriber drop to the device. Frequently, they have a tuner capable of receiving cable channels other than 2-13 (e.g., midband, superband, and hyperband channels). Even though a device may be cable compatible, it may still require an external descrambler to receive scrambled channels such as the premium pay channels or pay-per-view channels.

Cable Converter Box: Equipment often provided by a cable company in a subscriber's home that allows access or controls interference to cable services.

Cable Loading: Adding coils of wire at specific intervals along a cable in order to improve transmission quality. Cable pairs are often unloaded before they can be used for high-speed applications.

Cable Modem: Modem designed for use on cable TV coaxial cable to provide a theoretical bandwidth of up to 10 Mbps, although actual speeds are usually much lower. Cable modems share bandwidth with other units in the area, and are always on.

Cable Signal Leakage: Excessive levels of radio frequency (RF) energy that leak from cable television systems. Leak can cause interference to communications users, including safety service users such as aviation, police and fire departments. FCC rules specify the maximum RF leakage, and require that cable television systems be operated within certain guidelines.

Cable Television Channel Classes: Class I Source is a television broadcast signal that is being presently transmitted to the public and conveyed to the cable system for retransmission to the public, direct connection, off-the-air or obtained indirectly by microwave or by direct connection to a television broadcast station.

Cable Television Relay Service (CARS): The relaying of television, FM radio, cablecasting and other signals on a microwave frequency band to a terminal for distribution over CATV or over cable line.

Cable Television Transmission: The transmission, usually for a fee, of television signals, including signals that originate at over-the-air television stations, to consumers on a wired network.

Cable, Coaxial: A cable consisting of one or more tubes each of which has a wire contained within, and insulated from, a surrounding conductor. Large numbers of individual circuits can be carried by a coaxial cable by means of multiplexing.

Cable/Cable Television: A broadband communications technology in which multiple television channels as well as audio and data signals are transmitted either one way or bidirectionally through a distribution system to single or multiple specified locations. Uses coaxial cable to transmit programmes. Direct-by-wire transmission to homes from a common antenna to which these homes are linked. Cable companies provide the service in most cases. Distinguished from television reception through a roof-top antenna that picks up the broadcast signal. The only acronym was CATV, denoting community antenna television.

Cablecasting: Origination of programming, usually other than automated alphanumeric services, by a CATV system.

Cache Memory: A high-speed, buffer-type memory filled at medium speed from the main memory. Programmes and instructions found in the cache memory can be operated at higher speeds without the necessity of loading another segment.

Cache: In a processing unit, a high-speed buffer storage that is continually updated to contain recently accessed contents of main storage. Its purpose is to reduce access time. A holding area for data within the CD-ROM drive itself or on its interface board, that allows the system a method for matching data transfer rates and presentation speed requirements.

CAD Computer-Aided Dispatch: PublicsSafety dispatching with computers aiding in the process. This aid may be a simple display of pertinent information on a screen, up to the actual selection and notification of field unit(s) by the computer. 9-1-1 systems may be interfaced with CAD systems.

Call Accounting System : A computer, a magnetic storage device (floppy or hard disk), software and some mechanical method of attaching itself to a telephone system. A call accounting system is used to record information about telephone calls, organize that information and prepare reports - printed or to disk. The information it captures about phone calls typically includes from which extension the call is coming, which number it is calling (local or long distance), which circuit is used for the call (WATs, MCI, etc), when the call started, how long it lasted, for what purpose the call was made (client or project, etc). A call accounting system may also include information on incoming calls - which trunk was used, where the call came from, which extension took the call, if it was transferred and to where and how long it took.

Call Centre: An organisation whose major role is to handle phone calls (mainly from business customers) on behalf of one or (usually) several other large companies. They commonly use computer networks to give them access to that firm's databases, and to keep records of all calls they handle.

Call Data Record (CDR): Record of a placed call. A CDR includes the time the call was placed and the duration of the call.

Call Detail Record: When the 9-1-1 call is terminated by the PSAP operator, the ANI will automatically print out on the printer located at the PSAP. The printout will contain the caller's telephone number, the workstation number, the time the call came into the PSAP, the time it was answered by a telecommunicator, the time the call was transferred, if applicable, the time the call was terminated, and the trunk number associated with the call. Printouts of the ALI display will print out as soon as the call is answered.

Call Splashing: A practice in which a customer requesting operator service is handed off ("splashed") to their preferred operator service provider at a servicing centre located in a city other than where the customer is. This usually results in incorrect information about the originating location of a long distance call and in overcharging. This practice has been a particular problem in the U.S., and is associated with a proliferation of alternate operator service providers in that country.

Call Transfer: A call that is transmitted from number of calls for each PSAP.

Call-by-call Selection: The ability to switch calls to individual trunks, rather than trunk groups, and to transmit necessary information to the specific trunk-type necessary to complete the call.

Called Line Identification: A facility provided by a switched network in which the network confirms for the calling terminal, the telephone number of the line to which the call has been connected.

Calling Card: A telecommunication credit card with an AuthCode for using a long distance carrier when the customer is away from their home or office (ANI).

Calling Line Identity (CLID): A digital network feature where identity information from the device making a call is interpreted by the device answering the call. This is usually given in that the form of the telephone number of the person who is calling you.

Calling Name Delivery: Provides the ability during call setup to deliver the name of the calling party from the originating to the terminating switch or the name of the connected party from the terminating to originating switch.

Calling Party Pays: A billing method in which a wireless phone caller pays only for making calls and not for receiving them. The standard American billing system requires wireless phone customers to pay for all calls made and received on a wireless phone.

Camera: In television, an electronic device utilizing an optical system and a lightsensitive pick-up tube to convert visual images into electrical impulses.

Canadian Radio-television and Telecommunications Commission (CRTC): The federal regulatory authority for commercial radio and television broadcasters, cable system operators and telecommunications common carriers. Its primary objective is to preserve and enhance the communications system in Canada in the interest of all Canadians.

Candle Power: A measure of intensity of a light source in a specific direction.

Canned Programme: A software programme written to meet the expected customer needs of a certain application. Opposite of custom programmes.

Capability: Data processing equipment characteristic by which one machine may accept and process data without conversion or code modification.

Carrier: A carrier is a local (intra-LATA) or long distance (inter-LATA) telecommunications service providing organization. A waveform, pulsed or continuous, that is modulated by another information bearing waveform.

Carrier Access Tariff (CAT): The CAT - which all interexchange carriers, including telephone companies must pay for access to the utility (local) network - consists of one or more network access components (charges for switching and aggregation, recovery of start-up costs, etc.) and a contribution component to subsidize the rates for basic local telephone service.

Carrier Detect: The information as to whether or not the modem senses a carrier, like a fixed-line dialling tone or a data/fax services enabled on a GSM subscription.

Carrier Detect Threshold: A way of measuring how well a modem can detect valid data over noisy phone lines. It is measured in negative dBm's (decibel-milliwatts). The bigger the number (the more negative) the better. For example,45 dBm is better than40 dBm.

Carrier Hotel: A new or renovated structure built to collocate telecommunications equipment and antennas owned and operated by separate, even competing, telecommunications companies and Internet providers.

Carrier Identification Code - CIC: A three digit number used with Feature Groups B and D to access a particular IEC's switched services from a local exchange line. One or more CIC codes are assigned to each carrier. (i.e. there may be multiple CICs per ACNA).

Carrier Modulation: A signal at some fixed amplitude and frequency which is combined with an information bearing signal in the modulation process to produce and output a signal suitable for transmission.

Carrier Non-compatible Applications (CNCA): Applications which rely on metallic facilities (i.e., copper) with direct current continuity to provide service. Certain older applications, such as some provided by alarm companies, energy monitoring companies and other users of telemetry, could not generally be multiplexed, carried over digital facilities (i.e., fiber optics) or transported over radio facilities.

Carrier Service Provider: Company offering telephone and data communications between points in a state or in one or more countries. The Regional Bell Operating Companies (RBOCs) are example of carriers.

Carrier Services (CS): A wholesaling organization within Bell Canada, created in November 1992, that provides telecommunications services - at arm's length from the rest of the company - to the intermediary telecommunications market. These suppliers include: carriers and resellers; cellular and personal communications systems providers;

terminal equipment providers; the cable TV industry; and the message exchange industry.

Carrier Signal: Frequency in a communications channel modulated to carry analog or digital signal information.

Carrier System: A method for providing several communications channels over a single path. Accomplished by modulating the data, voice or video transmissions onto a higher frequency carrier wave, then recovering it at the receiving end through a process of demodulation .

Casual Calling: Allow any ANI (including undefined ANIs) to access a given carrier. For example, if the originator is calling from a non-coin phone, they may dial 1010555+destination number and have the call routed through WorldCom and billed to the originating phone

Casual Customer: Any person or organization that dials any CIC Code. (Not necessary to presubscribe to the carrier.)

Categories of Service: Basic and enhanced, as defined by the Federal Communications Commission (FCC). Basic service refers to transmission capacity for the movement of information; for example residential telephone service. Enhanced service combines basic service with computer processing; for example Electronic Yellow Pages.

Cathode Ray Tube (CRT): A vacuum tube display in which a beam of electrons can be controlled to form alphanumeric characters or symbols on a luminescent screen, for example, by use of a dot matrix.

CATV- Community Antenna Television: A broadband communications system capable of delivering multiple channels of entertainment programming and nonentertainment information from a set of centralized antennas, generally by coaxial cable, to a community. Many cable television designs integrate microwave and satellite links into their overall design, and some now include fiber optics.

CAV - Constant Angular Velocity: A disk that rotates at a constant rate of speed. Examples are hard drives, floppy disks, magneto-optical discs and some videodiscs. A CAV videodisc permits access to video within seconds, allows for up to 54,000 still frames, or may contain up to 30 minutes of full motion video (or any combination of stills and video).

CCITT: Consultative Committee on International Telegraph and Telephone; An international standards group.

CCL: Connection Control Language: A scripting language that allows the user to control a modem.

CCTV: Closed-Circuit Television. The system for sending cable signals to subscribers or designated locations.

CD-Audio: Also called CD-DA for Compact Disc-Digital Audio. The use of CDs to record music in digital audio format. The disc holds a sequence of audio tracks. Each can be a very high-fidelity stereo recording. These discs can be played on conventional CD players, CD-I systems and at least some CD-ROM drives. Standards for this are called the Red Book.

CD-I: 1. Compact Disc-Interactive. Stores text, audio, video, images and animation. Requires a CD-I player and will not work on a regular CD-ROM player. **2.** This interactive multimedia system, developed by Philips and Sony, connects to a television and stereo audio system. The standards for this are called the Green Book.

CDMA (Code Division Multiple Access): Digital telephone technique that splits a wireless signal into discrete packets of data, spreads them over a range of frequencies and then reassembles the information at the receiving end.

CDPD (Cellular Digital Packet Data): Radio technology that uses the existing digital cellular network to transmit data to mobile users. Based on TCP/IP, CDPD has a transmission speed up to 19.2 kbps. CDPD is sometimes called wireless IP. Data are bundled into units, or packets, and transmitted during breaks in cellular telephone conversations.

CDR Call Detail Records: Call data generated by the PBX in the form of an ASCII file that includes records of outgoing and incoming calls, who made or received the calls, incoming and outgoing locations of the calls, call length, time call took place and other information. May be stored in a buffer box.

CD-R: CD-Recordable Term used to describe special players and media which enable the creation of a single CD-ROM, written from the PC as if it were a magnetic disk drive. The end product, however, is a read-only disc: it cannot be erased or written over. Therefore, this technology is also known as "write-once CD."

CD-ROM Compact Disc - Read Only Memory: CD-ROM discs can store a variety of data types including text, colour graphics, sound, animation and digitized video that can be accessed and read through a computer. A disc can store up to 600 megabytes of data, much more information that can be stored on a 3.5 inch compute disk, which hold up to 1.4 megabytes. This makes CD-ROM an inexpensive medium for storing large amounts of data. Because CD-ROM was not designed to store digitized, full-motion video, compression technology is important in compressing data to fit on a disc as well as decompressing data for playback.

CD-ROM XA: CD-ROM Extended Architecture: A compact disc standard that permits the interleaving of compressed audio and video tracks for sound and animation synchronization. Based on the Yellow Book, it also uses some elements of the Green Book (CD-I).

CD-ROM: A laser-encoded optical memory storage medium, defined by the Yellow Book standard.

CD-WO - Compact Disc-Write Once: A term that describes compact discs that can be written to directly (rather than mass produced) with a laser recorder. Recent developments allow the CD-WO to be appendable. CD-WO media is physically defined by the Orange Book standard, Part II, and a proposal for the logical format has been submitted to ECMA by the Frankfort Group.

Cell: Basic geographic unit of a cellular telephone system. A large territory is divided into smaller areas or cells, each equipped with a low-powered radio transmitter/receiver. Size of a cell is determined by terrain, transmission power and anticipated customer load. As a wireless telephone moves from one cell into another, a computer at a Mobile Telephone Switching Office transfers the phone call to a new cell and radio frequency.

Cell Site: Location where wireless antenna and network communications equipment are placed.

Cellular Mobile Radio Telephone System: Also called "Cellular." A high capacity land mobile telephone system wherein channels assigned to the system are divided among several geographical "cells" covering a defined service area. A cellular system is capable of re-using the same channels in different cells within the service area. The use of many small cells in an area, with low transmitter powers, permits the intensive re-use of channels, thereby increasing system capacity.

Cellular Mobile Radio: A radio-based system providing exchange telephone service to a station located in an auto or other mobile vehicle or device (for example briefcase). Radio circuits transmitted to/from a base radio station cover a specific geographical area. As the vehicle or device moves from one area to another, different base radio stations handle the call.

Cellular Radio: Cellular Radio is the technology that has made wide scale mobile telephony possible - before cellular radio the problem with the mobile phone as a concept was how to get large numbers of users to share small amounts of radio spectrum. Cellular radio solved this problem by allowing the re-use of the same radio frequencies by assigning them to cells which were far enough apart to prevent noticeable interference.

Cellular Technology: This term, often used for all wireless phones regardless of the technology they use, derives from cellular base stations that receive and transmit calls. Both cellular and PCS phones use cellular technology.

Center Clipper: Variable attenuator which is used to eliminate any residual echo left by the echo canceller. A key difference between one canceller and another is the manner in which this center clipper operates. In a high quality canceller, the center clipper will operate very rapidly and smoothly, resulting in no residual echo during double-talk and no clipping of syllables. The center clipper is in essence a level-activated switch. Signals above the threshold level are passed unaltered and signals below the threshold are blocked. When speech is present in both directions, the center clipper tends to mutilate the speech signal, adding audible amounts of harmonic and intermodulation distortion. This distortion is often referred to as "glitch" and sounds remarkably like its name when it occurs. The transmit signal can be totally chopped out if the level of the transmit signal drops below the estimated level of returning echo.

Centi Call Seconds (CCS): CCS is a unit of the average traffic intensity of a facility during a period of time, a CCS is 100 call seconds of traffic during one hour. Therefore a single traffic source, e.g., one call that generates traffic 100% of the time produces 36 CCS of traffic per hour, i.e., 3600 seconds of traffic every 3600 seconds. An equivalent amount of traffic could also be generated by 10 sources that only generate traffic 10% of the time. That is, 10 sources of traffic generating 3.6 CCS each, contributes the same total traffic as a single 36 CCS traffic source. An alternative measure for traffic is erlangs where 1 erlang equals 36 CCS.

CENTRal EXchange (Centrex): Centrex is a LEC-provided switching service for business customers that permits station-to-station dialing, listed directory number service, direct inward dialing and station number identification on

Central Office (CO): Telephone company's building where end users' lines are joined to switching equipment that connects other end users to each other, both locally and via long distance carriers. The central office contains the associated inside plant network elements required to perform this function, such as distribution frames, interoffice facility termination points, and so on. Also known as End Office and Entity.

Central Processing Unit - CPU: The unit of a computer that includes circuits controlling the interpretation and execution of instructions.

Centralized Automatic Message Accounting (CAMA): Automatic message accounting (AMA) equipment that serves several central offices in recording data of customer-dialled long distance calls.

Centrex: A telephone business service provided by a local phone company from a local central office and provides features directly to each phone at a business without using an on-site PBX .

Centum call seconds (CCS): A traffic volume unit of measurement equivalent to 100 call-seconds. This unit is used in traffic study work, as it permits easier manipulation than seconds or minutes.

CEPT: European Conference of Postal and Telecommunications Administrations. The CEPT format defines the 2.048-Mb/s European E1 signal made up of 32 voice-frequency channels.

CEV (Controlled Environment Vault): Large, underground water- and weatherproof enclosure containing communications transmission gear.

CFDA - Catalog of Federal Domestic Assistance: The CFDA is a government-wide compilation of federal programmes, projects, services and activities that provide assistance or benefits to the American public. The primary purpose of the CFDA is to assist users in identifying programmes that meet specific objectives of a potential applicant, and to obtain general information on federal assistance programmes. The catalog is published once yearly, usually in June. An update occurs around December.

CFR - Code of Federal Regulations: The CFR is the "book" of federal laws and regulations. Usually referenced like this, 34 CFR 74.137. The "34" indicates that the subject of the regulation is education. The "70.137" refers to a specific paragraph.

CGI (Common Gateway Interface): Standard that allows Web servers to run search engines and other external applications.

Channel bank: **(1)** A part of the carrier system that performs the first step of modulation. **(2)** A multiplexer that modulates a group of channels into a higher frequency band and, conversely, demultiplexes the higher frequency band into individual channels. It can break a signal into the equivalent of 24 analog voice grade and/or 56 Kbps digital channels.

Channel Capacity: The maximum information rate which can be accommodated by a given channel. Channel capacity is generally measured in bits per second and may be stated in many other units. For example, it is often expressed in equivalent voice conversations. In addition, it may be stated in baud when specific terminating equipment is mentioned.

Channel Mileage Charge: Monthly leased rate for circuits between telephone company (telco) central offices.

Channel Service Unit (CSU): Channel Service Units (CSUs) and Data Service Units (DSUs) are required to connect digital customer premises equipment (CPE) to carrier networks. A CSU is network channel terminating equipment (NCTE) attaching as CPE to telephone company's digital circuits, and protecting the network from harm. Other CSU functions include line conditioning and equalization, error control (e.g., bipolar signal violations), and the logical ability to respond to local and network loop back circuit testing commands.

Channel Termination Charge: Fee associated with a T1 for the circuits feeding into a telco central office.

Channel: **(1)** The smallest subdivision of a transmission system by means of which a single type of communication service is provided, for example, a voice channel or a data channel. **(2)** A communications path via a carrier or microwave radio. **(3)** In data communications, a path for electrical transmission between two or more points. **(4)** Within a computer, the electronic paths along which data flows between the input-output units of a computer and the customer premises equipment (CPU).

Character: **(1)** Any alphabetical letter, digit or special symbol. **(2)** In data transmission, the representation of a letter number or symbol by a specific code made up of binary digits.

Character Generator: An alphanumeric text generator, a typewriter like device, commonly used to display messages on a television set. Chyron is a brand name for a character generator which is often mistakenly used to cover all character generators generically. Some sophisticated models also include colour, graphics, and mass memory for text storage.

Character-oriented: A communications protocol or transmission procedure that carries control information encoded in fields of one or more bytes.

Charge-Coupled Device - CCD: A solid-state device used in many television cameras to convert optical images into electronic signals. These imagers are organized into rows and columns called pixels. The charge pattern formed in the CCD pixels when light strikes them forms the electronic representation of the image.

Checksum: A number that represents a larger group of numbers in order to check for errors in data transmission. It is commonly used when downloading a programme, as well as in error control protocols. The checksum is the result of a mathematical equation, such as adding all the numbers in a block together.

Chips: Miniaturized microprocessors built on a single piece of silicon. [Typically, less than 1/2-inch square, they contain all the essential elements of a central processor, including the control logic, instruction decoding and arithmetic processing circuitry. Microprocessor chips are combined with memory and I/O integrated circuit chips to form a microcomputer, which usually fill no more than a single printed circuit board.]

Chip Set: A group of important IC chips on a modem (or other computer peripheral) that are all made by the same manufacturer. While there are many companies that make modems, there are only a few that make the chips for them. Because the chip manufacturer is making the chips for many companies, they produce more chips, and the price of the chips is lower than if each company produced their own. This decreases the price of the modems on the market.

Choppiness: Circumstance in which a caller's words are intermittently cut off, creating a situation of gaps in the voice transmission. Choppiness makes it difficult or impossible to have a "normal" conversation.

Chroma Key: In colour television, an electronic matting process of inserting one image over a background. Used very commonly with weathercasters who are standing in front of a blank wall painted process blue. The electronics remove the blue and insert the weather map so that on the television screen the two images merge and the weathercaster appears to be standing in front of a large map painted on the wall.

Chrominance Signal: The colour signal component in colour television that represents the hue and saturation levels of the colors in the picture.

Churn: The term used to describe turnover rate of subscribers to a service or product.

Circuit: A path for the transmission of electromagnetic signals; includes all conditioning and signalling equipment.

Circuit Associated Signalling: Circuit Associated Signalling is a technique that uses the same facility path for voice and signalling traffic. Historically this approach was selected to avoid the costs of separate channels for signalling and because the amount of traffic generated by signalling is small compared to voice, minimizing the chance for mutual interference. Circuit associated signalling can be contrasted with some common-channel signalling systems that use completely separate packet switched networks for signalling traffic.

Circular Polarization: A mode of transmission in which signals are downlinked in a rotating corkscrew pattern. A satellite's transmission-capacity can be doubled by using both right-hand and left-hand circular polarization.

Circulation (FCC term): An FCC term, circulation is the procedure whereby items are routed to Commissioners for notation voting without a need for discussion at an open or closed agenda meeting. Voting is done electronically from each Commissioner's office.

City Wide Digital Centrex: A city wide digital centrex is a capability to serve multiple business locations within a single NXX (exchange code), using multiple LEC central office Centrex switches. Outside callers are unaware that multiple business locations are involved.

Class of Service (COS): **(1)** Telephone service distinctions which include: rate differences between individual and party lines, flat rate and message rate, and restricted and extended area service. **(2)** A subgrouping of telephone customers or users for the sake of rate distinction or limitation of service.

Clean Power: Power circuits free of electromagnetic interference or noise. This may be involve placing special filters on individual circuits, installing specially shielded cable inside conduits or placing power conduits as far as possible from electric motors and other devices that could produce strong electromagnetic fields.

Clear Channel: A clear channel protects stations designated as Class A stations from objectionable interference within their primary and secondary service areas. The secondary service areas of the stations may extend outward for a distance of up to 750 miles at night. To provide this wide area service, Class A stations operate within a power range of 10 to 50 kilowatts.

CLEC: Competitive (or Certified) Local Exchange Carrier - the Telecommunications Act of 1996 opened the door for smaller companies to compete with the ILEC (Incumbent LECs), such as RBOCs (Regional BOCs) for local, long distance, international, internet and entertainment .

Client Server Architecture: Network structure, sometimes called two-tier architecture, in which each computer or process on the network is either a client or a server. In peer-to-peer (P2P) architecture, each node has equivalent responsibilities. Client servers also refer to a computing system that splits the workload between desktop workstations and one or more larger computers joined in a network.

Client/Server: A network architecture that lets a user at a PC request information or applications from another computer over a LAN .

Client: Computer that requests files or services from a server computer.

CLIP: Caller Line ID Presentation. A code that is sent over the phone lines in some areas when a person makes a phone call. This code includes the phone number of the person making the call. Some modems are able to understand this signal, and let you know who is calling you before you answer the phone.

Clipping: Situation where the system cuts off the first part of the first word in a sentence.

CLIR: Caller Line ID Restriction. The ability to block someone who you're calling from seeing your number.

Clock: A repetitive signalling device used to control a synchronous computer.

Closed Captioning: A service for persons with hearing disabilities that translates television programme dialogue into written words on the television screen.

Closed Circuit Television - CCTV: A private television system in which signals are sent usually via cable, to selected viewing points throughout the distribution system but are not broadcast to the public. The signal does not have to meet FCC commercial specifications.

Closed User Group (CUG): A number of users of a public switched communications service who have the ability to communicate with one another without interference from others.

Closed-circuit Television (CCTV): A system in which a signal is transmitted from a point of origin to only those receivers who have previously arranged access to it. Examples of its use are: lectures by professors in educational institutions, theatre television, sports, and video conferencing.

Cluster controller cluster controller: A device that handles the remote communications processing for multiple terminals or workstations.

CLV - Constant Linear Velocity: A disc that rotates at a varying rate of speed. Examples are CD-Audio, CD-ROM, CD-I, CD-ROM XA, and some videodiscs. CLV videodiscs may contain up to one hour of full motion video, but still frames and quick access time are forfeited.

CMOS: Complementary Metal Oxide Semiconductor. A chip which uses small amounts of electricity. It is used typically on battery-powered computers and to save configuration information on other computers when they are turned off.

Coaxial Cable - Coax: A type of metal cable used for broadband data and cable systems. It has excellent broadband frequency characteristics, noise immunity and physical durability. Consisting of a center conductor in the form of a tube which carries broadband signals by guiding high-frequency electromagnetic radiation, insulating dielectric, conductive shield, and optional protective covering.

Coaxial Cable (COAX): A type of cable commonly used in cable television systems which is composed of two concentric conductors: an inner wire, and an outer braided sleeve.

Co-Channel Interference: Interference on a channel caused by another signal operating on the same fichannel.

Codec: A COder-DECoder converts analog signals, (voice or video), into digital form (1 or 0) for transmission over a digital medium and, upon reception at a second codec, reconverts the signals to the original analog form. Two codecs are needed - one at each end of the channel.

Coding Violation (CV): A transmission error detected by the difference between the transmitted and the locally calculated bit-interleaved parity.

COE (Central Office Equipment): Switching systems and equipment found in a telephone company central office.

COI: A type of call whereby the person being called agrees to pay the charges. This is also referred to as "reversing the charges".

Coin Phone: A coin-operated pay phone with restricted access to some services (e.g. International calling). Coin phones have subclasses of Public, Semi Public, and Private.

Cold Boot: **(1)** First software initialization of the computer. **(2)** Software loading and checking just after the computer has been turned on.

Collaborative Learning: Collaborative learning involves a group working together through technology to delve into content. Students can electronically access other students, the instructor and resources.

Collect: A call that is paid for by the receiving/destination phone number. Requires approval/authorization of the person being called.

Colocation: Placing telephone switching equipment, antennas or Internet data equipment owned by separate companies at a single site operated by a third party. The third party provides normal and stand-by power and facility air conditioning for colocation customers.

Colour Bars and Tone: A colour standard test pattern used by the television industry to adjust equipment to standard levels. The tone is generated at a certain preset frequency so that audio levels can be set.

Colour Burst: In NTSC terminology, refers to a burst of approximately nine cycles of 3.58 MHz subcarrier on the back porch of the composite video signal. This serves as a colour synchronizing signal to establish a frequency and phase reference for the chrominance signal.

Colour Graphics Adapter (CGA): Equipment which provides 200 vertical x 600 horizontal pixel resolution for digital (rather than analog) video signals.

Colour Signal: Any signal at any point in a colour television system for wholly or partially controlling the chromaticity values of a colour television picture.

Colour Subcarrier: In NTSC colour, the 3.58 MHz subcarrier whose modulation sidebands are interleaved with the video luminance signal to convey colour information.

Colour Transmission: A method of transmitting colour television signals which can reproduce the different values of hue, saturation, and luminance which together make up a colour picture.

Combining Network: A passive network which permits the combining of several signals into one output with a high degree of isolation between individual inputs; commonly used in CATV headends to combine the outputs of all processors and modulators into a single coaxial cable input.

Command Line: On Unix host systems, this is where you tell the machine what you want it to do, by entering commands.

Commercial Leased Access: Manner through which independent video producers can access cable capacity for a fee.

Common Channel Interoffice Signalling (CCIS): A method in which labeled messages convey signalling and call completion information over a single circuit, leaving other circuits free for voice, data or video transmissions.

Common Control Switching Arrangement (CCSA): Network service that directs inward and outward dialing typically with a seven-digit code. Originally designed as a feature for private networks.

Common Intermediate Format (CIF): The type of coded video frame transmitted when using CCITT recommendation H.261 coding methods. CIF is 30 frames per second, 325H x 288V pixels.

Common Management Information Protocol (CMIP): CMIP is the OSI protocol for network management. A structure for formatting messages and transmitting information between reporting devices (agents) and data collection programmes, developed by the International Standards Organization and designated ISO/IEC 9596.

Communications: Communications is the process of representing, transferring, interpreting or processing information (data) among persons, places, or machines. Communications implies a sender, a receiver, and a transmission medium over which the information travels. The meaning assigned to the data must be recoverable without degradation.

Commucications Assistant (CA): A person who translates conversation from text to voice and from voice to text between two end users of Telecommunications Relay Service (TRS). This service allows a person with hearing or speech disabilities to communicate with anyone else via telephone at no additional costs. CA supersedes the term "TDD operator."

Communications Programme: A programme that controls a modem, and has features that allow the user to do such things as upload, download, etc. It is similar to a terminal programme but more sophisticated. An example is Trumpet WinSock for connecting to the Internet, and Windows HyperTerminal.

Communications Satellite Corporation (COMSAT): A United States company created by an act of Congress in 1962 to provide communications via satellites. COMSAT leases satellite circuits to many American companies and is active in international communications through partial ownership in the International Telecommunications Satellite Organization (INTELSAT) and the International Maritime Satellite Organization (INMARSAT).

Communications Satellite: Relay system in orbit above earth for telecommunications signals (voice, video, data); require earth stations to transmit and receive signals at the ground locations. Commonly called a "bird."

Communications Software: A programme that tells a modem how to work.

Communications Terminal: Any device which generates or receives electrical or tone signals that can be transmitted over a communications channel.

Community Antenna Television (CATV): A service through which subscribers pay to have local television stations and additional programmes brought into their homes from the antenna via a coaxial cable.

Community of Interest (COI): The interest shown by customers in one exchange in calling customers in another exchange, as measured by calling patterns. COI is an important criterion for Extended Area Service (EAS), which eliminates long distance charges by linking two or more telephone exchanges to form one common local calling area.

Compact Disc (CD): A five-inch disc on which a digital audio signal is inscribed so that it can be read optically by a laser beam device in a computer or CD player.

Compatible: Describes different hardware devices that can use the same software or programmes without modification, or with appropriate software.

Competitive Access Providers: Common carriers who provide local service and compete against local telephone companies' access services that connect customers to long distance companies.

Competitive Local Exchange Carrier (CLEC): Any company or person authorized to provide local exchange services in competition with an Incumbent Local Exchange Carrier. A CLEC provides similar or identical telecommunications services to the ILEC.

Competive Access Providers: Common carriers who provide local service and compete against local telephone companies' access services that connect customers to long distance companies. These carriers often use fiber optic networks.

Composite Video Signal: Transmission incorporating luminance, colour and synchronizing information.

Compress: To make data take up less space. Archiving programmes do this, which means that files will take less time to transfer with modems. Many modems now have the ability to automatically compress the information they send and receive.

Computer: A device capable of solving problems or manipulating data by accepting data, performing prescribed operations on the data and supplying the results of these operations. Various types of computers are: analog computer, digital computer, calculator.

Computer Conferencing: Allows individuals at different locations to communicate with each other through computers. This could be through a chat room, e-mail, a classroom environment created by software. It might include text, audio, video, or shared work spaces on which all participants can type or draw.

Computer Supported Telephony (CST): It is based on that the ability of the telephone system and computer to exchange information. One example of an application is the ability to present on screen information such as scripts, simultaneously with an incoming call. The scripts are based upon information gathered about the caller prior to the telephone being answered. This is generally achieved by either menu systems or by a identification are of the incoming line which the caller has dialled or his calling line identity.

Computer Telephony Integration (CTI): Extension of computer-based intelligence and processing over the telephone network to a telephone. CTI lets you interact with computer databases or applications from a telephone. It also enables computer-based applications to access the telephone network. Computer telephony makes computer-based information readily available over the worldwide telephone network from your telephone.

Computer-aided Design (CAD): Automation of the performance of various operations according to graphic design specifications through the use of a special computer and peripherals.

Computer-aided Manufacturing (CAM): Automation of the performance of various operations according to manufacturing specifications through the use of a special computer and peripherals.

Computer-assisted Instruction (CAI): An application in which a stand-alone personal computer or system is used to teach. Applications usually involve a dialogue between students and software programmes which inform students of their mistakes in a real-time manner.

Concatenate: The linking together of various data structures, for example two bandwidths joined to form a single bandwidth.

Concatenated STS-Nc: A signal in which the STS Envelope Capacities from the N STS-1s have been combined to carry an STS-Nc Synchronous Payload Envelope (SPE). It's used to transport signals that don't fit into an STS-1 (52 Mb/s) payload.

Concatenation: **(1)** To unite in a series; to link together; to chain. **(2)** The linking of transmission channels (phone lines, coaxial cable, optical fiber) end-to-end.

Conditioning: **(1)** To bring to a standard. **(2)** Addition of equipment to voice grade lines to provide for data transmissions at specified minimum values of line characteristics, in ranges from C1 to C4 (the best).

Conductor: In electrical circuits, a conductor is any material that readily permits a flow of electrons (electrical current) through itself. Analogously, optical fibers are sometimes said to conduct light waves and are also referred to as conductors.

Conference Call: A connection established among three or more stations in such a manner that each of the stations is able to communicate with all the others.

Conferencing: A term used to indicate when several network users communicate on a particular subject. Conferences can be "live" or conducted via a BBS.

Configuration: The interconnection and programming of independent machines or equipment to operate as a system.

Connect Time Charges: Most networks charge users for the time they spend on-line. These are referred to as connect time charges. The amount charged depends on the network's fee schedule. Users must also pay a separate fee if the call to connect is toll.

Connect Time: Time period during which a user is utilizing a computer on-line - or directly connected with the computer.

Connector: A device which connects the output of one equipment unit to the input of another.

Consortium: Voluntary group affiliated for a purpose. Consortia is plural.

Contention: Condition on a communications channel or in a peripheral device when two or more stations try to either transmit at the same time or access a resource simultaneously.

Continuous Presence Video: Simultaneous and continuous pictures of participants.

Contract: A legally-binding agreement between a vendor and a customer to provide Products, Services or Features in a specified quantity and quality, for a specified price, during a specified period of time.

Contract Tariffs: Services and rates based on contracts negotiated with individual customers, but theoretically available to all customers. AT&T has filed several hundred contract tariffs.

Contribution: An amount charged to offset the costs of providing local telephone service.

Control Room: A room separate from a studio in which the director, the technical director (TD), the audio engineer, and other technical and programme assistants control programme production.

Control Unit (CU): Central processor of a telephone switching device.

CONUS-Contiguous United States: The 48 contiguous U.S. states. Used primarily to designate the operating range or authorization of a satellite or radio facility.

Convergence: Convergence means that providers of communication systems can deliver products and services that compete with the products and services now delivered by other networks. One example would be a cable company providing local phone service or a local phone company providing video services.

Conversation Time: The portion of total holding time on a call during which the conversation, text or transmission of data takes place.

Conversational Mode: Operation of a data processing system in which a sequence of alternating entries between a user and the system takes place in a manner comparable to a conversation between two persons.

Cooperative Learning: This learning model is based on specific group rewards for team members' learning and task specialization. Students work together to solve problems and locate information, Courseware: Software used in teaching. Often used to describe computer programmes designed for the classroom.

Core Competency: Core competency is the in-depth, primary, embedded set of capabilities, technologies and processes which constitute an organization's collective "know how", in providing customer value and access to markets.

Corporation for Open Systems (COS): COS is a nonprofit organization composed of manufacturing, service, and user organizations in the computer communications area. Seeks to facilitate the development of the international, multi-vendor marketplace through the development, introduction, and verification of OSI and ISDN standards and by ensuring vendor equipment interoperability.

Counter: Device which tallies the number of occurrences of an event.

Country Code: A one-, two- or three-digit number used for international dialing. [The first digit is always the world-zone number. Subsequent digits further define the geographic area.]

CPE (Customer Premises [or Provided Equipment): Telephone devices such as handsets and PBXs located at the customer's site that interface with the public network. It includes equipment such as modems, terminals and routers supplied by the telephone company, installed at customer sites and connected to the telephone network.

Cracker: From hacker and safe cracker. A hacker who breaks into computers

Cramming: A practice in which customers are billed for enhanced features such as voice mail, caller-ID and call-waiting that they have not ordered.

Crash: An abrupt, unplanned computer system shutdown caused by a hardware or software malfunction.

Crawl Space: Space for textual messages usually at the bottom of the television screen.

Crawl: A visual technique; electronically generated words or graphics that move horizontally or crawl across the screen, usually at the bottom.

Credits: The names of people on whom the production can be blamed. Electronically generated words that usually move horizontally up the screen like a scroll, or inserted a page at a time.

Credit and Collections Policy: Guidelines and procedures which Bell follows to collect the money owed by its customers.

Credit Classification: Customers are assigned a credit classification based on Bell's assessment of their ability and willingness to pay their bills promptly. This classification determines the amount of long distance calls they will be permitted to charge to their account, as well as the amount of time they will be given before they are contacted to request payment.

CREN: Corporation for Research and Educational Networking.

Crosstalk: **1.** Undesired transfer of signals from one circuit to another circuit. **2.** The phenomenon whereby a signal transmitted on one circuit or channel of a communications system is detectable or creates an undesirable effect in another circuit or channel.

Cross Connect: **1.**in a premises distribution system, equipment used to terminate and administer communications circuits. In a wire cross connect, jumper wires or patch cords are used to make circuit connections, between horizontal and backbone wiring segments. **2.** in transmission systems a patch panel for connecting circuits.

Crossbar Switch: A type of analogue electro-mechanical central office switch.

Cross-subsidy: The practice whereby long distance revenues subsidize local telephone service, with the goal of keeping local service affordable.

Crosstalk: Transmission noise caused by energy "leaking" from one channel to another on the same facility.

CSV: Short for comma-separated values, another name for the comma-delimited format of data representation.

CTI (Computer-Telephony Integration): Merger of computers with traditional telecommunications equipment. Caller ID, which automatically retrieves and displays customer information from a central database, is a CTI application.

CTS: Clear To Send. This is when the modem lets the other computer know that it can send information to the other computer.

Current Loop: Transmission technique that recognizes current flows, rather than voltage levels.

Cursor: A symbol on the display of an editing or display terminal that can be moved up, down, or sideways and indicates where the next character is to be located or where "home" or beginning is located.

Customer Attitude Survey: Annual surveys of residence and business customers conducted by Bell to determine general perceptions and attitudes towards its services, equipment and image in the community.

Customer Information System (CIS): The Telco database which holds customer information such as service and product orders, installation dates, features used or invoice history. This information is pulled by IPS and other billing systems.

Customer Network: A collection of communications elements linking terminating equipment that supports one or more customer applications.

Customer Owned and Maintained (COAM): User provided and serviced communications equipment and its associated wiring.

Customer Premises Equipment (CPE): All telecommunications equipment (except pay phones) and, usually, wiring that is located at the users building.

Customer Service: A department in an organization that provides outbound services such as: technical assistance, help lines, product or account information, location of dealers, emergency responses, service information or complaint handling.

Customizable PIN: A PIN that gives you the ability to choose the specific numbers or character sequence.

Cut: A command that stops all action in actual production; or a visual technique for changing abruptly from one picture to an entirely different one; for example, quick cuts in which many different visuals appear rapidly one after another on the screen.

Cutover: The exact date/time that a phone number, circuit, etc. is scheduled to be (or was) moved from one implementation (carrier, etc.) to another. (e.g. moving an 800 number from MCI to WorldCom).

Cyberphobic: A person who is fearful of working in cyperspace. Cyberspace: Coined by science fiction writer William Gibson in the 1970s, it describes the virtual place of computer memory, networks, and multimedia.

Cyberspace: A term introduced by science fiction author William Gibson in 1984. "Cyberspace" is where human interaction occurs over computer networks, through Email, games or simulations.

D

D Type Channel Bank: A D type channel bank is channel termination equipment used for combining (multiplexing) individual analog channel signals on a time division basis. D type channel banks provide interfaces for "n" analog signal inputs. Each analog input signal is directed to a codec for en coding to PCM samples. A part of a Tl carrier system.

D1 and D2: Digital tape component and composite formats (respectively) used for professional video recording. D1 is costlier than D2. Both can go through many generations of dubbing without visible loss of picture quality.

D4 Framing Format: (1) Division of DS1-level circuit into 24 equal channels. [Each channel carrier digitizes voice and signalling information in eight-bit bytes. A D4 frame consists of 192 (8 X 24) information bits. In addition, to identify each of the 24 channels, a framing bit is added in the 193rd position. Each byte is updated 8,000 times per second. Thus, the transmission speed of a DS1 circuit is 1,544,000 Hz (193 X 8,000).] (2) Monitors the DS1 signals for either framing errors or bipolar violations (BPVs). BPVs are eliminated when the bit stream passes through interfaces such as a multiplexer, Automatic Protection Switch or the Digital Cross-Connect System (DCS). Since no end-to-end performance monitoring is available using BPVs, the line must be taken out of service to test for large errors.

DAA: Data Access Arrangement. A device used to connect modems to the switched telephone network.

Daemon: An otherwise harmless Unix programme that normally works out of sight of the user. On the Internet, you'll most likely encounter it only when your e-mail is not delivered to your recipient - you'll get back your original message plus an ugly message from a "mailer daemon" saying the message was undeliverable.

Daisy Chain: Connection of multiple devices in a serial fashion. [An advantage of daisy chaining is a savings in transmission facilities. The disadvantage is that if a device malfunctions, all other devices daisy-chained behind it are disabled.]

DAL - Dedicated Access Line: A non-switched circuit from the customer to a carrier.

D-AMPS (Digital AMPS): Digital wireless standard that uses digital TDMA but is also compatible with existing AMPS systems. It operates in the 800 and 1900 MHz bands.

Dark Fiber: Unused capacity in a fiber optic cable.

DARPA: Defence Advanced Research Projects Agency of the Pentagon. Replaced ARPA.

Data above Voice (DAV): Transmission system which carries digital data on a portion of the microwave radio spectrum above the frequency used for voice transmission.

Data Access Arrangement (DAA): Communication equipment furnished by a common carrier that allows attachment of privately owned data transmission equipment (DTE) to the common carrier network.

Data Center: Highly secure, fault-resistant facilities housing customer equipment that connect to telecommunications networks. The facilities accommodate Web servers, switches, routers and modem racks. Data centers support corporate Web sites and provide locations for CLECs, ISPs, ASPs, Web hosting companies and DSL providers.

Data Communications Channels v: OAM&P channels in SONET that enable communications between intelligent controllers and individual network nodes as well as internode communications.

Data Communications: (1) Transfer of information between a source and a destination via one or more data links, according to appropriate protocols. (2) Transmission and reception of data, often including operations such as coding, decoding and validation.

Data Compression: Some modems have the capability to 'squash' data so that it takes up less space. When another modem (that also has this capability) receives the data, it 'unsquashes' the data to its original form. By using data compression, a modem can send information faster. It's a lot like shorthand-all the information is still there, but it takes less space and is quicker.

Data Conversion: Process of changing information from one form of representation to another.

Data Coupler: A device to connect customer-owned modems or data sets to the regular telephone network. It functions by limiting the power applied to the line and providing network control and signalling.

Data Encryption Standard (DES): A cryptographic algorithm designed by the National Bureau of Standards to encipher and decipher data using a 64-bit key.

Data over GSM: Send digital data over the digital GSM networks.

Data Packet: Format in which data is transmitted over a network. The packet contains the data itself and information necessary to ensure the packet arrives intact at the intended destination.

Data Pbx: A digital switch that allows a user on an attached circuit to select from other circuits, usually one at a time and on a contention basis, for the purpose of establishing a through connection. [A data PBX is distinguished from a PBX in that only digital transmission, and not analog, is supported.]

Data Service Units (DSU): DSUs are channel service units (CSI's) and data service units (DSUs) are required to connect digital customer premises equipment (CPE) to carrier networks. A hardware device providing an interface between a digital line and a unit of data terminal equipment. DSUs provide transmit and receive control logic, synchronization and timing recovery across data circuits. DSUs may also convert ordinary binary signals generated by CPE to special bipolar signals. Bipolar signals are designed specifically to facilitate transmission at up to 1.544 Mbps rates over UTP cable, a media originally intended for 3 kHz, voice bandwidth signals.

Data Terminal Equipment (DTE): **(1)** Provides for the communications control function (protocol). **(2)** Any piece of equipment at which a communications path begins or ends.

Data Transmission Rate: The speed at which data travels. For example, data may be sent at 115,200bps. Same as transmission rate, transmission speed, data rate.

Data: Any and all information, facts, numbers, letters, symbols, etc. which can be acted on or produced by the computer.

Database: An organized compilation of computerized bits. [Formalized rules exist for the establishment, control and access of a database.]

Datalink Control: Second layer in the International Standards Organization reference model for Open Systems Interconnection (OSI).

Datapac Network: A common user, packet-switched data network provided by The Computer Communications Group of the Trans Canada Telephone System.

Dataphone Digital Service (DDS): A communications service of the Bell System in which data is transmitted in digital rather than analog form, thus eliminating the need for modems.

Dataphone: **(1)** A generic term to describe a family of devices to facilitate data communication. **(2)** An AT&T designation for a service which provides data communication over telephone facilities.

DB Loss: Decibel (dB) is a unit of measure of signal strength, usually the relationship between a transmitted signal and a standard signal source. Loss is measured when the signal received across a communication circuit is less than what was transmitted by the signal generator.

DBm: Decibel refers to one milliwatt. This is used to measure certain levels, such as transmit level.

DCE : Data Circuit Terminating Equipment. Sets up and maintains a data connection link over a communications medium. For example, a modem.

DDD - Direct Distance Dialing: Any switched telecommunication service (like 1+, 0++, etc.) that allows a call originator to place long distance calls directly to telephones outside the local service area without an operator.

Death Star Satellite: A fixed-orbit communications satellite which, because of its ability to transmit hundreds of television channels, poses a threat to the established cable television industry.

Debug: Checking the logic of a programme to isolate and eliminate the mistakes from a computer programme or other software.

Decibel (dB): A unit measuring the relative strength of sound or electrical power. The unit is useful to relate changes in loudness to changes in electrical power and vice versa. One decibel is the faintest audible sound. With respect to electrical power, it is generally used in measuring the loss or gain of power in a device or channel. One milliwatt is usually the electrical reference point for 0 decibels.

Decision Table: **(1)** A matrix of contingency plans with the actions to be taken.

Dedicated Access: A direct connection between a terminal and a service, network, or computer dedicated to the specific use of a particular customer.

Dedicated Access Line (DAL): A non-switched circuit or path connecting the customer's telephone equipment to the Telco switch with no intermediate switching functions by the Local Exchange Company (LEC).

Dedicated Data Channel: A data channel or circuit for the use of a particular customer.

Dedicated Line: A communications circuit or channel provided for the exclusive use of a particular subscriber. Dedicated lines are used for computers when large amounts of data need to be moved between points.

Dedicated System: Videoconferencing equipment, transmission circuits, and teleconferencing facilities that are permanent and used on a regularly scheduled basis as opposed to rented for a one-time or ad hoc event.

Default Routing: Provides for routing of 9-1-1 calls when there is an ANI failure. The call will be routed to a predesignated PSAP or seven digit number. This occurs when a particular 9-1-1 call cannot be selectively routed for any reason.

Default: A standard setting or action taken by hardware or software if the user has not specified otherwise.

Defect: A limited interruption in the ability of an item to perform a required function.

Definition: Also called resolution. The fidelity with which detail is reproduced by a television system ranging from a fuzzy to a sharp appearance.

Degradation: A deterioration in the characteristics of a signal or system.

Delay: Time it takes for a signal to go from sending station through the satellite to receiving station.

Delay Dial: A switching configuration whereby local equipment will wait until it receives the entire telephone number before seizing a circuit to transmit the call.

Delay Distortion: Noise or echo resulting from the non-uniform speeds of various signal components of transmissions through a transmission medium(s).

Demarc: (Demarcation Point) The point, jack or cross connect panel, at which ownership or responsibility for operating and maintaining facilities passes from one party to another.

Demarcation Point (Demarc): Point of connection between telephone company's system and customer premises.

Demodulate: To retrieve an information carrying signal from a modulated carrier. A demodulator is a device that removes the modulation from a carrier signal.

Demodulation: A process whereby a modulated signal is returned to its original form. A demodulator is a component of a data set or modem which converts analogue data to digital data by receiving tones sent over a communication line.

Demultiplexing: A process applied to a multiplex signal for recovering signals combined within it and for restoring the distinct individual channels of the signals.

Denial: Call condition that occurs when no circuits are available and a busy tone is returned to the calling party. This situation is distinctly different from delay in that denial is not time-related and can only be measured in terms of the percentage of calls denied.

Dense Wavelength Division Multiplexing (DWDM): DWDM is the higher capacity version of WDM, which is a means of increasing the capacity of fiber-optic data transmission systems through the multiplexing of multiple wavelengths of light. Commercially available DWDM systems support the multiplexing of from 8 to 40 wavelengths of light.

Deregulation: **(1)** A 1983 Federal Communications Committee ruling which freed the interexchange carriers from the need to file rate changes or seek authority from FCC to expand. AT&T was not deregulated because of its economic power and market dominance.

Descrambler: An electronic circuit that restores an intentionally scrambled video signal to its original standard form.

Diagnostic: Means of detection, discovery and further isolation of an equipment malfunction or a processing error.

Dial Access: **(1)** Connection through the public switched telephone network. **(2)** Means of providing a terminal switched access to a service, network or computer.

Dial Around: Long distance services that require consumers to dial a long-distance provider's access code (or "10-10" number) before dialing a long-distance number to bypass or "dial around" the consumer's chosen long-distance carrier in order to get a better rate.

Dial Exchange: An automated switching junction or central office. For example, a PBX permitting call placement by rotary or pushbutton dialing rather than by an operator.

Dial Level: The selection of stations or services associated with a PBX using a one- to four-digit code (for example, dialing nine for access to outside dial tone).

Dial Pulse (DP): A short, direct current signal which is produced by, or simulated to look like, the opening and closing of contacts in a rotary-dial telephone when numbers are dialled. Dial pulses control the action of telephone switching equipment.

Dial Repeating Tie Line/Dial Repeating Tie Trunk: A private line communications arrangement which links two or more points together and permits direct trunk to trunk connections without use of an attendant.

Dial Selective Signalling: A multipoint network in which the called party is selected by a prearranged dialing code.

Dial Tone: Ready To Place/Originate A Call. When the off hook indication is received at a central office, a dial tone signal is sent to the originating caller on a switched network to indicate that the switch is ready to accept a number.

Dial up - Dialup: To call another computer via modem. A connection or line reached by modem, as in "a dialup line."

Dialing Plan: A description of the telephone number assignments for customer use on a telecommunications network.

Dial-It Service: A telecommunications service that permits simultaneous calling by a large number of callers to a single telephone number. There is usually a fee for calls to 900 numbers or 976 numbers .

Dialled Number Identification Service (DNIS): The ability to identify the number to which the call was made. In a call centre, for example the call may come into a specific DDI number. The call is answered by an agent in an ACD group, and the system uses the DNIS to present the agent with a screen containing a script associated with that DDI number.

Dial-up Line: (1) A communications circuit that is established by a switched circuit connection. (2) Any circuit available over the public switched network.

Dial-Up Teleconferencing: Using public phone line to connect with a teleconference, either with or without operator assistance.

Dielectric: A non-conductive insulator material between the center conductor and shield of coaxial cable. The dielectric constant determines the propagation velocity.

Digit L: Digital L is another amplitude condition that represents a binary digit 0.

Digital Access Cross-Connect Switch (DCS): Digital switching device for routing time slots among multiple T1 ports.

Digital Audio Broadcasting (DAB): Radio broadcasting using digital modulation and digital source coding techniques.

Digital Carrier Systems: Digital Carrier Systems are carrier systems for digital signals that uses regenerative versus linear repeaters and time division multiplexing.

Digital Compression: A collection of techniques used to compress a stream of computer-generated digital information, allowing information to be sent using less bandwidth.

Digital Computer: A computer that operates on discrete data by performing arithmetic and logic processes on these data.

Digital Cross Connect System (DCS): DCS is a new generation of switching/multiplex equipment that permits per-channel DS0 (64 kbps) electronic cross-connection from one T1 transmission facility to another, directly from the constituent DSl signals. Commonly referred to as "DACS" (digital access and cross connect system), although this is a trademark of AT&T.

Digital Exchange Access (DEA): Digital Exchange Access service provides digital access between a customer's premises or other service point and the public switched telephone network.

Digital Media: Refers to any type of information in digital form including computergenerated text, graphics and animations, as well as photographs, animation, sound, and video.

Digital Modem: Component that supports communication over ISDN lines. These devices, sometimes called ISDN terminal adapters, convert the PCM-encoded digital output of analog modems into the signal's original analog waveform.

Digital Multiplex System (DMS): A means of utilizing technologies that provide digital switched service for voice and data transmission. DMS is characterized by the use of pulse code modulation (PCM) and time division multiplexing (TDM) throughout the switched network. It allows the direct switching of PCM signals used in transmission systems without their conversion to analog format.

Digital Private Network Signalling System (DPNSS): Allows the transfer of PBX facilities between PBXs, even of different makes.

Digital Signal: A digital signal is a signal (electrical or otherwise) in which information is carried in a limited number of different (two or more) discrete states. The most fundamental and widely used form of the digital signal is binary, in which one amplitude condition represents a binary.

Digital Signal (DS): (1) A nominally discontinuous electrical signal that changes from one state to another in discreet steps. **(2)** A signal that is time-wise discontinuous (i.e., discreet) and can assume a limited set of values. Antonym: analog.

Digital Signal Hierarchy: A series of standardized increments for multiplexing of digital channels in T-carriers an other types of carrier systems for digital transmissions. The North American DS hierarchy is structured differently in other global regions.

Digital Switched Network (DSN): A high-speed digital switched public network which allows business customers to access a huge range of calling capabilities (e.g., international telecommuting, videoconferencing, telemedicine, distance education and criminal identification) at prevailing long distance rates and discounts. DSN, which is available to customers who subscribe to Digital Exchange Access Service, Centrex Data or Integrated Services Digital Network (ISDN), is available in several countries around the world.

Digital Technology: Method of storing, processing and transmitting information through the use of electronic or optical pulses that represent binary digits or bits (0 and 1).

Digital Television (dtv): A new technology for transmitting and receiving broadcast television signals. DTV provides clearer resolution and improved sound quality.

Digital Termination Service (DTS): DTS is a service provided by some carriers permitting opera tors of private networks to use digital microwave equipment to gain access to carrier net works. The FCC has allocated a special microwave band for DTS.

Digital Transmission System: A transmission system whereby sound waves and other information are transmitted in a series of on and off pulses, and in which the signals can be regenerated. This type of transmission is sharper, clearer and quieter than analogue transmission.

Digital Video Effects - DVE: Video effects accomplished through digital devices that manipulate the video; e.g., page turns, revolves, boxes that zoom into and out of the picture, images that turn into pixels, etc.

Digital/Digitized: Any type of information that can be output, transmitted and interpreted as individual bits of binary information (the use of the numbers O and 1), using electrical or electromagnetic signals that can be modulated to convey their specific content. A TV picture will be more like a rectangle and have up to 1,080 lines of resolution, producing a crisper picture.

Digitize: The process of converting analogue signals to digital form.

Digitized Audio: Allows the incorporation of audio materials with other media to present information over a computer network or through the Internet. With this method, the audio is contained.Various software programmes "stream" the audio signal so that it can be heard as it is being said.

Digitizer: A device that converts an analog signal (either images or sound) into a digital signal that can be manipulated on the computer. Video capture boards convert video images from video sources such as the VCR or video camera, while sound digitizers take any sounds, the spoken word as well as music off of a cassette or CD player, and turn them into digital data. That data can be edited using sound editing and multimedia software.

Diode: A two-electrode electron tube or its semiconductor equivalent. [Usually employed as liquid crystal diodes (LCD) or light emitting diodes (LED) and are especially applicable to portable computers.]

Direct Broadcast Satellite (DBS)/DISH: A high-powered satellite that transmits or retransmits signals which are intended for direct reception by the public. The signal is transmitted to a small earth station or dish (usually the size of an 18-inch pizza pan) mounted on homes or other buildings.

Direct Call: A facility which avoids the use of address selection signals or typed dialing sequences. The network interprets the off-hook status or call request signal as an instruction to establish a connection with a single destination address previously designated by the user.

Direct Dialling Inward (DDI): DDI uses a small group of exchange lines to access a larger number of extensions. The first part of the number selects the line, whilst the last part gives the extension number. This method is very economical on exchange lines.

Direct Distance Dialing (DDD): A telephone system which enables users to directly dial telephone numbers outside the user's local exchange area without the aid of an operator.

Direct Inward Dialing (DID): DID is PBX-to-central office trunks that allow incoming calls to a PBX to ring specific stations without attendant assistance. DID greatly reduces the number of required console attendants.

Direct Mail: Any type of advertisement, brochure or printed piece delivered to a targeted audience, usually through the postal service.

Direct Outward Dialing (DOD): DOD is PBX-to-central office trunks that allow outgoing calls to be placed directly by PBX stations.

Direct Read After Write - DRAW: A laser based technology for recording data on a videodisk. direct response: Refers to direct mail and telemarketing campaigns.

Directional Microphone: A microphone that detects and transmits sound from only a certain direction. Useful in preventing unwanted sound from being transmitted.

Directory Assistance - DA: An information service whereby operators assist customers in obtaining the telephone number(s) they wish to call.

Disaster Routing: Capability of the telephone company, when notified by the PSAP, to reroute 9-1-1 calls to some other predesignated location during a disaster situation.

Disc: Preferred usage (spelling) of the term for reference to optical storage media, such as CD-Audio, CD-I, CD-ROM, videodisc, or WORM.

Discrete: Pertains to separate and distinct parts of data such as holes in a card or graphic characters.

Dish: Parabolic antenna. Primary element of a satellite earth station; sends and/or receives satellite signals. Usually bowl-shaped; concentrates signals to a single focal point. The antenna cross section exposed to the signal is the aperture.

Disk Drive: A computer data storage device in which data is stored on the magnetic coating (similar to that on magnetic tape) of a rotating disk.

Dispersion: In dispersive media, dispersion are complex signals are distorted because the various frequency components which make up the signal have different propagation characteristics and paths. Due to the finite conductivity of copper, wire or cable media for guided wave transmission is fundamentally dispersive. Dispersion limits the upper bit rate that a medium can support by distorting the signal waveforms to the extent that transitions from one information state to another cannot be reliably detected by receiving equipment, (e.g., logical 1 logical 0 value changes).

Display: The visual presentation on the indicating device of an instrument.

Dissolve: Gradual transition from one television picture to the next by fading out one picture and simultaneously fading in another.

Distant Signal: A television channel from another market imported and carried locally by a cable television system.

Distortion: (1) Any change from the original wave form or signal. (2) Normally, non-predictable changes which interfere with interpretation of the result.

Distributed Data Processing: Data processing in which some or all of the processing, storage, and control functions, in addition to input-output functions, are situated in different places and connected by transmission facilities.

Distributed Function: The use of programmable terminals, controllers, and other devices to perform operations that were previously done by the processing unit, such as managing data links, controlling devices, and formatting data.

Distribution Systems: Any programme that can be received by the satellite antenna, can be distributed into several viewing areas. The distribution system is one or more wires that run from the earth station control room, into several classrooms or conference rooms. Broadband wiring systems use a single coaxial cable, while baseband systems use several twisted-pair wires. Both systems must be custom designed for each location, using high output amplifiers and exact cable lengths.

Distributor: A person/company that distributes signals from a satellite carrier and provides that transmission either directly to individual subscribers for private home viewing or to other programme distribution companies for transmission.

Divestiture of AT&T: The settlement resulting from the U.S. Justice Department's anti-trust suit against AT&T in which that company was ordered to divest itself of its Bell operating companies (BOCs). The settlement also stipulated that the BOCs would be responsible for providing long distance service within their operating territories. With the implementation of the settlement in 1984, ownership of the 22 BOCs (previously owned by AT&T), was consolidated into seven regional holding companies. AT&T was left with two main subsidiaries: AT&T Communications and AT&T Technologies.

DLC (Digital Loop Carrier): Device that links services from carrier fiber to subscriber copper, usually housed in the point of presence office or an outdoor cabinet. Each DLC servers 600 to 2,000 subscribers.

DMS Data Management System: A data base managed by the telephone company which includes ANI and ALI information.

DMS (Digital Multiplex System): A family of switching systems that provides digital circuit-switched service for voice and data transmission, and packet switched service for data transmission. DMS is characterized by the use of pulse code modulation (PCM) and time division multiplexing (TDM) throughout the switched network. The system allows the direct switching of PCM signals used in transmission systems without their conversion to analogue format.

Docket Number (FCC term): A number assigned to a proceeding opened by the issuance of either a Notice of Proposed Rule Making or a Notice of Inquiry, or if an adjudicatory or tariff proceeding, has been instituted. Since January 1, 1978, the docket numbers indicate the year they were initiated and the Bureau which initiated the docket.

Domestic Satellite: A satellite that provides communication services primarily to one nation.

Dot: To impress the Net veterans encountered, parties say "dot" instead of "period." For example: "My address is john at site dot domain dot com."

Dot File: A file on a Unix public-access system that alters the way the user or the messages interact with that system. For example, a user's .login file contains various parameters for such things as the text editor used when a message is sent. When an ls command is done, these files do not appear in the directory listing; do ls -a to list them.

Double Speed Drive: Refers to a CD-ROM drive that will read certain kinds of data faster than the standard requires (155KB/sec). Many drives now have 300KB/sec transfer rates (also known as twice the standard, or 2X); at least one claims 600KB/sec (4X).

Double-Talk: The situation where parties at both ends of a conference are speaking simultaneously. A quality echo canceller will provide a continuous speech path in both directions during double-talk.

Down: When a public-access site runs into technical trouble, and you can no longer gain access to it, it's down.

Down Time: Period during which a computer, communications line or other device is not operating correctly because of mechanical or electronic failure.

Downconverter: A device used to lower the frequency of any signal.

Downlink: The part of a satellite system that includes the satellite itself, the receiving earth station and the signal transmitted from the satellite to earth stations.

Download: **1.** Transfer data from a main computer or memory to a remote computer or terminal. **2.** There are several different methods, or protocols, for downloading files, most of which periodically check the file as it is being copied to ensure no information is inadvertently destroyed or damaged during the process. Some, such as XMODEM, only let you download one file at a time. Others, such as batch-YMODEM and ZMODEM, let you type in the names of several files at once, which are then automatically downloaded.

Downstream: An audio or video signal travelling from the cable TV headend to a subscriber point in the community.

Drive Bay: The opening in a computer chassis designed to hold a floppy drive, hard drive, CD-ROM drive, tape drive or other device. May be half-height or full-height, exposed or internal.

Drop Off: The number of customers who discontinue telephone service.

Drop: **(1)** The portion of an outside telephone plant which extends from the telephone distribution cable to the subscriber's premises. **(2)** A connection point for a terminal on a line.

Drop-Outs: Black or white lines or spots appearing in a television picture originating from the playback of a video tape recording.

Dry circuit: A circuit which transmits voice signals and carries no direct current.

DSA: Data Services Adapter, an alternative interface to PCMCIA for connecting to a fax or data terminal. The Siemens S1 uses a DSA

DSL (Digital Subscriber Line): Technology that dramatically increases the digital capacity of ordinary telephone lines. The distance from the customer to the telco central office determines DSL speeds. Asymmetric DSL (ADSL) is for Internet access, where fast downstream is required, but slow upstream is acceptable. Symmetric DSL (SDSL) is best for connections that need high speed in both directions. DSL provides "always-on" operation. At the Central Office, DSL traffic is aggregated in a unit called the DSL Access Multiplexor (DSLAM) and forwarded to the appropriate ISP or data network. DSL can compete with cable modems in bringing multimedia and 3-D to homes and small businesses.

DSR: Data Set Ready. This indicates that the modem is on, and ready to accept input from the computer.

DSX-1: May refer to either a cross-connect for DS1 rate signals or the signals cross-connected at DSX-1.

DSX-3: May refer to either a cross-connect for DS3 rate signals or the signals cross-connected at DSX-3.

DTE: Data Terminal Equipment. This is computer equipment which is not directly responsible for communicating, for example, the computer itself and printers.

DTMF - Dual Tone Multiple Frequencies: Standard telephone signalling technique which can be used through any transmission medium of voice grade or better. he technique is often used for remote switching control functions.

DTR: Data Terminal Ready. The DTR signal is sent from the computer to the modem, to let the modem know that the computer is ready to communicate.

Dual Band Capability: Many receivers are capable of both C and Kuband operation.

Dual Mode: Mobile telephone that can be used on both digital and analog networks.

Dual-Tone Multiple Frequency (DTMF): The generic name for the tone signalling scheme used to signal from telephones to switching equipment, in which 10 decimal digits and two auxiliary characters are represented by selecting two frequencies of the following group: 697, 770, 852, 941,1209,1336,1447 Hz.

Dub - Dupe - Duplicate: The duplication of an electronic recording. Dubs can be made from tape to tape in video, or from record to tape in audio. In video, one generation of quality is usually lost between each duplicate except when using high grade broadcast equipment and one inch wide tape. Usually a video tape that appears fuzzy and the colors have lost clarity, it is a 3rd, 4th, or 5th generation tape - in other words, a copy, of a copy, of a copy, of a copy, of a copy.

Dumb Terminal: (1) Conversational display terminal with limited resident intelligence. (2) Terminal capable of receiving and transmitting data from a host computer over a communications network.

Duplex: In a communications channel the ability to transmit in both directions.

DWDM (Dense Wavelength Division Multiplexing): Simultaneously transmitting two or more optical signals having different wavelengths in the same direction over one fiber and then separating them by wavelength at the receiving end.

Dynamic Bandwidth Allocation: Process that automatically increases or decreases the bandwidth of a channel to accommodate changes in data flow.

Dynamically controlled routing (DCR): A technique of changing transmission routing patterns dependent on network load. DCR provides significant cost efficiencies, increased flexibility and network survivability relative to the traditional hierarchical means of routing.

E

Earth Station: Equipment on earth that can transmit or receive satellite communications. In general usage, this term refers to receive-only stations.

Echo: An interference present on telephone circuits in which transmitted signals are reflected back to the source from the terminating end. This is particularly troublesome in voice communications and is overcome by the installation of echo suppressors in the transmission path which absorb the echo when each party is talking.

Echo Canceller: Eliminates audio transmission echo. A telephone line echo canceller produces a synthetic replica of the echo it expects to see returning and subtracts it from the transmitted speech. The replica it creates is based on the transmission characteristics of the telephone cable between the echo canceller and the telephone set.

Echo Reduction: A newer method of echo control, developed in 1988, uses attenuation in a new way to subjectively reduce the returned echo without the mutilation (choppiness, level drops, distortion) found in suppressers or center clippers. It rapidly and momentarily applies a variable amount of attenuation in between transmitted speech peaks (where the echo would be audible).

Echoplex: A method of checking and compensating for echos in network terminals that are operating in the two-way simultaneous mode.

ECSA (Exchange Carrier Standards Association): An organization that specifies telecommunications standards for ANSI.

EDGE (Enhanced Data Rates for Global Evolution): Proposed upgrade of TDMA-networks that promises data transmission rates as high as 384 kbps.

EDI: Electronic Data Interchange. Commonly transferred by Internet or X.400 networks

Edit: **(1)** To prepare data for a later operation. **(2)** Functions such as the rearrangement or the addition of data, the deletion of unwanted data, format control, code conversion and the application of standard processes such as zero suppression.

Educational Access Channel: A cable television channel specifically designated for use by local education authorities.

Edutainment: Multimedia designed for teaching. It's based on the theory that learning doesn't have to be boring.

E-Layer: A heavily ionized signal-reflecting region location 50-70 miles above the surface of the earth, within the ionosphere.

Electrical Signal: An electrical signal is a signal consisting of an electrical current (i.e., a flow of electrons) that varies with time or space in accordance with specified parameters.

Electrically Alterable Read Only Memory - EAROM: A type of memory that is nonvolatile, like ROM, but can be altered, or have data written into it, like RAM.

Electromagnetic Interference: Any electromagnetic energy, natural or man-made, which may adversely affect performance of the system.

Electromagnetic Spectrum: The frequency range of electromagnetic radiation that includes radio waves, light and X-rays. At the low frequency end are sub-audible frequencies (e.g., 10 Hz) and at the other end, extremely high frequencies (e.g., X-rays, cosmic rays).

Electro-Mechanical Pen: A device that has an electronic pen with a mechanical arm for producing free-hand information that can be sent over a telecommunication channel, usually a telephone line.

Electronic Bidding: A process by which bidders in an auction use computers to place their bids.

Electronic Blackboard or Whiteboard: A device that looks like an ordinary blackboard or whiteboard, but has a special conductive surface for producing free-hand information that can be sent over a telecommunications channel, usually a telephone line.

Electronic Book: Computer programme (often called an electronic book) that uses text, graphics, animation and audio to guide the user through an instruction or teaching process, an electronic "help-desk."

Electronic Bulletin Board: A system located on a computer network which allows users to post or receive information; it facilitates file sharing.

Electronic Editing: In videotapes, a process by which picture and sound elements (live or pre- recorded) are joined together without physically cutting the tape. In sophisticated editing suites, this is done by computer.

Electronic Funds Transfer (EFT): An electronic system that transfers money and records financial transactions, replacing the use of paper.

Electronic Key Telephone Set (EKTS): Any key telephone with a built-in microprocessor which allows access to PBX-like features as well as access to multiple CO lines and uses two- to four-pair wiring.

Electronic Mail (E-Mail): E-Mail allows the user to send a message via a computer instantly to one or many persons around the world. E-mail users typically have a "mailbox" on a network or a videotext system where other users can send messages to be retrieved by the recipient.

Electronic Switched Network (ESN) Service: ESN service is a private network service that provides user organizations with a uniform numbering plan and numerous call-routing features. The electronic tandem switching functions are furnished by either PBX or Centrex switching equipment.

Electronic Switching System (ESS): A type of analogue central office telephone switching system.

Electronic Tandem Network (ETN): (1) A private network in which the network switch functions as a PBX and automatically connects the calling office to the called office through tandem-tie trunks.

Elevation: The location of the satellite in the sky from your viewing site. How high above the horizon the satellite is, which is called elevation or altitude which is measured in degrees.

Eligible telecommunications carrier: Telecommunications carrier considered eligible to receive universal service support because it offers phone service to all customers throughout a service area without preference and advertises the available supported services in the mass media.

E-mail: The term for private messages sent as files from one computer to another, either over a local area network (LAN), or via modem over the phone lines. E-mail is like having your own private mail box on a network. Used as both a noun and verb. Mail can be sent between Internet and commercial services such as American On Line.

EMI (Electromagnetic Interference or Interface): Unintentional, undesirable responses or performance degradation of electrical equipment casued by radiation from electrical or magnetic fields.

Emulator: Hardware or software built into a computer system which causes the system to appear as if it were another system.

En banc: An informal meeting held by the Commission to hear presentations on specific topics by diverse parties. The Commissioners, or other officials, question presenters and use their comments in considering FCC rules and policies on the subject matter under consideration.

Encoder: A device that electronically alters a signal (encrypts) so that it can be clearly seen only by recipients that have a decoder which reverses the encryption process.

Encoding: **(1)** Inscribing or imprinting Magnetic Ink Character Recognition (MICR) characters on checks, deposits and other documents to be processed by a MICR reader. **(2)** The introduction of data on a medium such as a magnetic strip on plastic cards.

Encryption: An encoder electronically alters a signal so that it can be clearly seen only by recipients who have a decoder to reverse encryption. Selective addressability/scrambling designates receivers to descramble a signal. Each decoder has a unique "address."

End of Tape Sensing: A form of sensing (optically or mechanically) that automatically stops the tape transport at the end of tape or upon breakage of tape.

End Office (EO): EO is a LEC (BOC or an ITC) switching system within a LATA where local loops to customer stations are terminated for purposes of interconnection with each other and with trunks.

End User: The ultimate last user of a telecommunications system whether or not it is a student within a school, business or a subscriber on a cable television system.

Enhanced Service Providers: A for-profit business that offers to transmit voice and data messages and simultaneously adds value to the messages it transmits.

Enhanced Services: Services using network facilities and computer processing that: act on the format, content, code, protocol or similar aspects of transmittal information; provide additional or restricted information or. involve subscriber interaction with stored data.

Enterprise Number: **(1)** A unique telephone exchange number that permits the terminating party to be automatically billed for incoming calls. **(2)** A toll-free number.

Entrance Facilities: **1.** in a premises distribution system, the point of interconnection be tween the building wiring system and external telecommunications facilities (LEC networks, other buildings, etc.). Bellcore defines the interface with LEC networks as end-user points of termination (POT). **2.** has a further specific meaning in interstate access, entrance facilities for interstate access (ENFIA).

Envelope Capacity: The number of bytes the payload envelope of a single frame can carry. The SONET STS payload envelope is the 783 bytes of the STS-1 frame available to carry a signal. Each virtual tributary has an envelope capacity defined as the number of bytes in the virtual tributary less the bytes used by VT overhead.

EPS - Electronic Performance Support System: A computer supported just-in-time information system that might hold instruction manuals and other information on how to perform the tasks at hand.

Equal access (EA): (1) The concept - enforced by the 1984 Modified Final Judgement (MFJ) - that all Interexchange Carriers (IXC) must have the same access to the local BOC facilities as AT&T enjoys; provided as Feature Group D interconnection. **(2)** The arrangement whereby the BOCs provide trunk side connections to an End Office (EO), Automatic Number Identification (ANI), answer supervision, dial pulse or DTMF signal recognition.

Equalization: (1) Procedure to compensate for fluctuation in circuit amplitude, delay or distortion and to produce a flat frequency response rate. **(2)** In data communications, a compensation for the increase of attenuation within frequency.

Equipment Room: In a premises distribution system, an equipment room is a special purpose room(s), with access to the backbone wiring, for housing elecommunications, data processing, security, and alarm equipment.

Equivalent Service: Multiline telephone service in which calls are automatically completed at the next available line of a group when the dialled number is busy.

Ergonomics: A discipline that promotes the consideration of human factors in the design of a working environment and its components (heat, light, sound, equipment).

Erlang: A measure of the average activity on a line or group of lines, e.g. exchange lines, extension or operator consoles, over a period expressed as a number of simultaneous calls.

EROM - Erasable Read-Only Memory: In a computer, the read-only memory (ROM) that can be erased and reprogrammed.

Error: When there is line noise and one or more characters are changed. This is especially noticeable when downloading or uploading a programme. In this case the error must be detected, and the data must be resent.

Error Burst: Results of an event that causes a lengthy stream of consecutively transmitted bits to be defective.

Error Correction: The ability of a modem to notice errors in transmission, and to resend incorrect data.

Error Free Seconds (EFS): Measurement of the performance of T1 lines, expressed as EFS per hour, day or week.

Error Rate: Ratio of the number of signal elements (or data) incorrectly received to the total number transmitted. (2) The probability of an error occurring during the transmission of a message.

Errored Second (ES): A one-second interval containing one or more errors.

Error-Free Seconds (EFS): Ratio of the number of seconds in which there are no bits in error to the total number of seconds in the measurement interval.

ESD (Electrostatic Discharge): Discharge, which can damage integrated circuits, of a static electric charge on a surface or body to the ground.

ESN Emergency Service Number: A three-digit number that is assigned to the caller's telephone number in the tandem office translations. The emergency service number routes the call to the proper PSAP. PSAPs also receive a display of the ESN information.

ESS Electronic Switching System: Computerized switching of telephone calls used by the telephone company.

Ethernet: One of the oldest LAN technologies which has been highly successful and is still popular. It was originally developed by Xerox, Intel and DEC. It was developed to run over coaxial cable although it can now run over twisted pair. It uses CSMA/CD and is similar to the IEEE 802.3 standard in that they share the same cable specification and can communicate with each other. Ethernet can run at up to 10Mbits/s.

Ex Parte Presentation: Any communication addressing the merits or outcome of a particular proceeding made to decision-making personnel, which, (1) if written, is not served on the parties to the proceeding, or (2) if oral, is made without opportunity for the parties to the proceeding to be present.

Exchange (EX): **(1)** A room or building equipped so that telephone lines terminating there may be interconnected as required. The equipment may include manual or automatic switching equipment. **(2)** A telephone switching center; an aggregate of traffic-carrying devices, switching stages, controlling and signalling means at a network node that enables subscriber lines and/or other telecommunication circuits to be interconnected as required by individual callers. **(3)** The territory served by an exchange, within which local service rates apply; also known as the exchange area or local service area.

Exchange Access: Offering access to telephone exchange services or facilities for the purpose of the origination or termination of telephone toll services.

Exchange Carrier (or local exchange carrier LEC): An exchange carrier is any company, BOC or independent which provides intra-LATA telecommunications within its franchised area.

Exclusion: A feature on some telephone systems permitting a user to exclude or prevent other users from gaining access to a line or channel.

Execute: To perform the operations required by an instruction, command or programme.

Expedite: The acceleration of a processing procedure, e.g., due date, that is different from the norm.

Exterior Gateway Protocol (EGP): Inter-networking protocol for passing routing information among autonomous systems.

Extended superframe format (ESF): Use of the Cyclical Redundancy Check-6 (CRC-6) Code to measure actual logic errors rather than format errors.

External Binary Coded Decimal Interchange Code (EBCDIC): A transmission system used by several IBM and IBM-compatible data terminals which consists of eight data bits, each of which represents a particular number, letter or character.

Extract: A data synopsis from a given system which is passed to another system to complete processing.

Extranet : One-to-one connections over the Internet that are not accessible to all; mainly set up by a business for their customers or business partners.

F

F2F - Face to Face: When you actually meet those people you been corresponding with/flaming.

Facilitator: In adult education (androgogy), the person responsible for a class who acts as a guide and resource to the students. The person responsible for the local component of a video teleconference site is normally called a facilitator.

Facilities Based Private Switched Network Services: Facilities Based Private Switched Network Services is a private network for which LECs and IXCs dedicate physical switching and transmission facilities for the exclusive use of a particular customer.

Facilities-Based Carrier - FBC: A carrier that uses its own facilities to provide service, in contrast with resellers, that purchase the services of other carriers and then retail the services to customers.

Facility: A transmission path between two or more locations without terminating or signaling equipment.

Facsimile - FAX: A devce which uses a form of electronic transmission allowing movement of hard-copy documents from widely separated geographic areas via a telecommunications channel, usually a telephone line. Usually called a FAX machine now but previously was called a telecopier.

Facsimile: (1) A system for the transmission of a picture, drawing or other document by converting it into coded electrical signals which are subsequently converted into a replica of the original image at the receiving end. **(2)** The replicated image of picture, drawing or document.

Failure: A termination of the ability of an item to perform a required function. A failure is caused by the persistence of a defect.

FAQ - Frequently Asked Questions: A compilation of answers to these. Many Usenet newsgroups have these files, which are posted once a month or so for beginners.

Fast Ethernet: Any of the three versions of 100Mbps Ethernet competing to become an IEEE standard. Grand Junction Networks Inc., HP, and a consortium of vendors are proposing solutions for the 100Mbps Ethernet standard.

Fast Packet: Fast Packet is a term referring to a number of broadband switching and networking paradigms. Implicit is the assumption of an operating environment that includes reliable, digital, broadband, nearly error free transmission system.

Fault tolerance: The level of ability within a programme or system to operate properly even if errors occur.

Fax: **(1)** Abbreviation for facsimile. **(2)** Reference to either the service or the actual machines by which a copy of a document or picture may be transmitted

Feature Group A (FGA): **(1)** A service that uses off-network access lines (ONAL). **(2)** A level of dial-up service in which subscribers have to dial a full local subscriber number to connect to the IXC, then have to key out (using DTMF) their personal authorization code followed by the distant number required.

Feature Group B (FGB): **(1)** A dial-up service that gives no hardware answer code which means call timing may be inaccurate. **(2)** A service that uses off-network access trunks (ONAT) which eliminate most off-network access line difficulties and greatly improve transmission quality (for local offices).

Feature Group C (FGC): **(1)** A dial-up service that uses off-network access trunks which eliminate most off-network access line difficulties and greatly improve transmission quality (for local tandem offices).

Feature group D (FGD): **(1)** A dial-up service employing a coding method to enable telephone customers to choose their long distance network and use the same number of digits whichever carrier chosen. (2) Uses off-network access trunks (ONAT).

Feature Groups: The different types and qualities of public switched network connection between local telephone companies and long distance companies.

Feedback: In video; wild streaks and flashes on the monitor screen caused by re-entry of a video signal into the switcher and subsequent over-amplification. In audio, piercing squeal from the loudspeaker caused by the accidental re-entry of the loudspeaker sound into the microphone and is over-amplified. Feedback can also occur when using a conference telephone while the TV volume is too loud.

Feeder Cables: The coaxial cables that take signals from the trunk line to the subscriber area and to which subscriber taps are attached.

Fiber Optic Cable: Bundles of hair-thin glass filaments through which light can travel. Fiber offers greater transmission capacity with less interference than metal cables.

Fiber Optics Transmission System (FOTS): A transmission system utilizing hair-thin glass fibers through which light is transmitted. Information is transferred by modulating the transmitted light. These modulated signals are detected by light-sensitive semiconductor devices. The signals are regenerated to relay the information and demodulated to retrieve the information.

Fiber Optics: A method for the transmission of information in which light is modulated and transmitted over high-purity, hair-thin filaments of glass. The bandwidth capacity of fiber optic cable is much greater than that of copper wire.

Fiber To The Curb (FTTC): Network with optical fiber from the telephone switch to a curbside distribution point, where it is converted to copper wire.

Fiber To The Home (FTTH): Network with optical fiber from the telephone switch to the subscriber's residence.

Fiber-optic Cable: A bundle of thin filaments of glass or other transparent materials used as the medium for transmitting coded light pulses that represent data, images or sound.

Fiber-optic Transmission System (FOTS): A means of sending data by coded light pulses through small diameter glass fibers.

Field: One-half of a video frame two fields equal one frame or a full video screen. One field will contain all of the odd or even scanning lines of the picture. Field Blanking Interval: The period provided at the end of the field picture signals primarily to allow time for the vertical sweep circuits in receivers to return the electron beam completely to the top of the raster before the picture information of the next field begins.

Fifo (first in-first out) Queuing: Method where the next item to be retrieved is the item which has been waiting the longest.

File Server: A station or computer dedicated to providing file and mass data storage services to the other stations on the local network.

File Transfer Protocol: Internet protocol that allows files to be transferred over a network.

File: **(1)** An organized, named collection of records treated as a unit. **(2)** The storage media on which these records are kept.

Filename Extension: A three-letter (usually) code at the end of a filename that give some indication as to the type of file in non-Macintosh environments that lack icons or other methods of identifying files. Common extensions include .txt for text files, .hqx for BinHexed files, .sea for a self-extracting file, and .sit for Stuffit files.

Film at 11: One reaction to an overwrought argument: "Imminent death of the Net predicted. Film at 11."

Film Chain: Also called film island, or telecine. Consists of one or two film projectors, a slide projector, a multiplexer, and a television camera. Converts film and slides to television signals.

Finger: An Internet programme that lets you get some bit of information about another user or computer, provided they have first created a .plan file.

Firewall: Computer security that attemps to keep crackers out.

Firmware: Computer programmes that are embodied in a physical device that can form part of a machine.

Fixed Position System: Low cost systems limited to reception from one satellite and one band. Motorized System Receives programmes on different satellites by adjusting the dish position. Automated Systems Microprocessor controlled for instant movement to satellites (positions stored in memory).

Fixed Satellite Service - FSS: The earth stations are not mobile. This service generally provides telephone and TV distribution.

Fixed Service: Radio-communications service between specified fixed points.

Fixed Stuff: A bit or byte whose function is reserved. Fixed stuff locations, sometimes called reserved locations, do not carry overhead or payload.

Fixed System: A permanent satellite receive and transmit system. The fixed system is put in place for regular use and broadcasts are made to the same sites repeatedly. The fixed systems are used for employee training, product introduction, meetings and other needs. Most fixed networks are owned by corporations such as Merrill Lynch, Hewlett-Packard, Sears, J. C. Penney, and General Motors and are not available to outsiders for videoconference use. However, they can receive teleconferences which are of interest to them.

Fixed Transfer: Allows an established 9-1-1 call to be transferred by a PSAP telecommunicator to another specific location or another PSAP. Fixed transfer is accomplished by a predesignated transfer button and uses the speed calling feature of the 9-1-1 tandem office.

Flame: On-line yelling and/or ranting directed at somebody else. Often results in flame wars, which occasionally turn into holy wars.

Flat Rate Service: A service which is provided at a fixed monthly charge regardless of usage.

Flate Rate: A method of pricing in which a fixed rate is charged for a given service, regardless of usage. The fixed monthly charge which a residential subscriber in a local exchange pays to be allowed to make an unlimited number of local calls is an example of a flat rate.

Floating Mode: A virtual tributary mode that allows the VT synchronous payload envelope to begin anywhere in the VT.

Pointers identify the starting location of the VT SPE. VT SPEs in different superframes may begin at different locations.

Flow Control: A method of controlling when information is sent. One method is Xon/Xoff, where a BBS will send information until your computer sends an Xoff (CTRL-S). It will resume sending information when you send an Xon.

FM Broadcast Band: The band of frequencies extending from 88 to 108 MHz.

FM Cable Service: The offering of FM radio signals over a cable system for a fee. A cable is connected to the subscriber's FM stereo receiver for service.

FM Microwave Radio: Ultra-high frequency often used to provide the return link in fully interactive systems (simplex). It can also be used in duplex to provide two-way fullmotion video and audio interactivity.

Follow-up: A Usenet posting that is a response to an earlier message.

Font: A complete set of characters for one style of one typeface (and traditionally, in metal type, in one size), including upper and lowercase letters, numerals, punctuation marks, and special characters. Often used to mean the software that renders a particular typeface. Sometimes used interchangeably with typeface. Typeface The full range of letters and other characters of a given type design. Usually includes all the weights and styles, but is sometimes used to mean just one weight and style.

Foo/foobar: A sort of on-line algebraic place holder, for example: "If you want to know when another site is run by a for-profit company, look for an address in the form of foo@foobar.com."

Footcandle: The unit of illumination equal to 1 lumen per square foot.

Footprint: The area in which a specific transmission can be received. Some footprints cover as much as one-third of the earth, such as satellite or cell systems.

Forced Disconnect: The call is automatically disconnected when the Public Safety Answering Point telecommunicator hangs up.

Forebearance: A provision of the Telecommunications Act that allows the CRTC to refrain from regulating those sectors for which it believes regulation is not necessary.

Foreign Exchange (FX): FX is a service that provides a circuit(s) between a user station, a PBX, or a Centrex switch, and a central office other than the one that normally serves the caller.

Foreign Exchange Line: Line offered by a common carrier in which the user in one central office is assigned a telephone number belonging to a remote central office to minimize long distance charges. [Charges for these lines vary from carrier to carrier.

Format: An established system standard in which data is stored.

Fortune Cookie: An inane/witty/profound comment that can be found around the Internet.

Forward Channel: Communications path carrying voice or data from the originating caller to the terminating destination.

Forward Error Correction: Technique for regenerating lost data transmissions or error messages; retransmission of any information by the transmitter.

Four-Wire Circuit: A circuit that has two pairs of conductors (four wires), one pair for the send channel and one pair for the receive channel; allows two parties to talk and be heard simultaneously.

Fractal Compression: Compression technique which uses real-time adaption of the numbers of bits allocated to different colors based upon the present scene.

Fragmentation: Storing parts of a file in disparate available space on a disk, rather than contiguously.

Frame: In time division multiplexing systems, Frame is a sequence of time slots each containing a sample from one of the channels carried by the system. The frame is repeated at regular intervals, and each channel usually occupies the same sequence position in successive frames.

Frame Relay: A high speed interface between switches and T1 or T3 multiplexers. Frame relay is a connection-oriented interface that initially will be incorporated into private T1 and T3 multiplexers. While some carriers have committed to offer public frame relay service, others consider frame relay to be an "interim technology" and are focusing on cell relay. T1 and T3 multiplexers equipped with frame relay will provide a packet-oriented, HDLC-framed interface to routers and X.25 packet switches. The packets will be routed to the proper destination by the multiplexers. Minimal protocol processing enables frame relay multiplexers to achieve high throughput. Initially, permanent virtual circuits will be supported; later, it is likely that switched virtual circuits services may also be provided by frame relay. The major advantage of frame-relay-equipped multiplexers is that only a single connection is required from the customer premises equipment to the multiplexer. Also, with frame relay support in multiplexers, users contend for bandwidth provided via the multiplexer, and thus line cost efficiencies can be improved.

Frame Store: A video storage and display technique where a single frame of video is digitized and stored in memory for retrieval and subsequent display or processing. An electronic device used to store still pictures; a highly sophisticated slide projector used to insert pre-produced still materials into a live production for visual enhancement. The graphic material can be words, graphs, quotes, or photographs.

Frame to Frame Differencing: Compression technique which encodes only the information that represents the difference between successive frames.

Framing: Method of distinguishing digital channels that have been multiplexed together.

Franchise Authority: The franchise authority is the local body,usually a local government enity, that enters into a contractual agreement with a cable company. A franchise agreement defines the rights and responsibilities of each in the construction and operation of a cable system within a specified geographical area.

Franchise: Authorization issued by a municipal, county, or state government entity which allows the construction and operation of a cable television system within the bounds of its governmental authority. The franchise area is the geographical area specified by a franchise where a cable operator is permitted to provide CATV service.

Freenet: An organization whose goal it is to provide free Internet access in a specific area, often by working with local schools and libraries. The first and preeminent example is the Cleveland Freenet. Freenet also refers to the specific Freenet software and the information services that use it.

Freephone: These numbers start 0800 and will not cost you money if you call from a land line. If you call from your mobile, call costs will vary and you will be charged.

Freeware: Software that doesn't cost anything. It can be distributed freely. However, the author still holds the copyright which means that the software can't be modified.

Freeze Frame Video: Freeze frame video is one frame of video, saved as an electronic slide. It can be transmitted by video over a network or saved in a video effects generator to display when it is needed to illustrate a concept.

Freeze Frame: Repeating or holding one frame so that it appears that the action has stopped.

Frequency: A measurement of the number of electromagnetic waves that pass a given point in a given time period. It is equal to the speed of light divided by wavelengths, and is expressed in Hertz (cycles per second).

Frequency Division Multiplexing (FDM): FDM divides the frequency bandwidth (spectrum) of a broadband transmission circuit into many subbands, each capable of supporting a single, full time communications channel on a non- interfering basis with other multiplexed channels. FDM multiplexing is generally suitable for use with analog carrier transmission systems.

Frequency Modulation (FM): Radio transmission covering 88-108 megahertz on the broadcast band. FM is less susceptible to interference than AM broadcasting, and is also used in other frequency bands for two-way communications in land mobile and marine services.

Frequently Asked Questions (FAQs): FAQs on Internet sites answer the most often asked questions.

FTP - **File-transfer Protocol:** A system for transferring files across the Internet. Anonymous FTP is a conventional way of allowing you to sign on to a computer on the Internet and copy specified public files from it. Some sites offer anonymous FTP to distribute software and various kinds of information. You use it like any FTP, but the username is "anonymous". Many systems will allow any password and request that the password you choose is your userid. If this fails, the generic password is usually "guest".

Full Duplex Audio Channel: An audio channel which allows conversation to take place interactively and simultaneously between the various parties, without electronically cutting off one or more participants if someone else is speaking. With a Half Duplex Audio Channel, only one party can speak at a time without cutting off the other end.

Full Duplex: Full duplex is a transmission path capable of transmitting signals in both directions simultaneously.

Full-motion Video: Not compressed. A standard video signal of 30 frames per second, 525 horizontal lines per frame, capable of complete action.

Fully Competitive Service: A service for which market forces are sufficiently strong to eliminate the need for service regulation (e.g., the sale and lease of terminal equipment).

Fully Dedicated Access: Long distance carrier access method in which a non-local call is carried by the long distance carrier via a dedicated trunk facility for both the first and last part of the call's journey, and on the same long distance carrier's network for the entire length of the call. Also referred to as "dedicated-to-dedicated" or "on-net to on-net."

Fully Interactive Audio/Video: Two or more video conferencing sites can interact with one another via audio and video signals. Two sites may be fully interactive without necessarily being full-motion sites.

Further Notice of Proposed Rule Making (FNPRM): A Commission term, a Further Notice of Proposed Rule Making is issued by the Commission to further clarify and seek more information and public comment on the Commission's proposed changes.

FX Foreign Exchange Line: The ANI telephone number is located in an area not within the geographical boundaries of the local 9-1-1 service area, but draws dial tone service from an end office within the 9-1-1 service area.

G

Garbage: Unwanted or meaningless information being stored in a file or used in a process.

Garbage in-garbage out (GIGO): Phrase used to describe quality of data input and output within a computer system; specifically, if input data is bad (garbage in) then the output data will also be bad (garbage out).

Gateway: A network element (node) that performs conversions between different coding and transmission formats. The gateway does this by having many types of commonly used transmission equipment to provide a means for interconnection.

General Packet Radio Services GPRS: Packet Switched data radio technology for GSM networks. GPRS connections are always open giving mobile terminal users the same kind of network availability they may be used to from corporate networks. There are no set up and clear down times associated with data calls made via GPRS. Terminals can therefore effectively become a part of the Internet.

Genlock: Ability of a device that handles video signals to synchronize itself to an external signal, as for overlaying graphics onto the incoming signal.

Geostationary Orbit: The revolutionary path traveled by a satellite in which the satellite travels in sync with the Earth's motion, so that it appears stationary in the sky. A stationary antenna located on Earth can remain pointed at the satellite at all times.

Geostationary Satellite: A satellite whose circular and direct orbit lies in the plane of the Earth's equator and which remains fixed relative to the earth.

Geosynchronous Orbit: Position over the equator that communication satellites assume; an area about 23,000 miles above the earth's surface where a satellite's velocity matches the rotation of the earth, causing it to remain stationary relative to a point on the earth.

GHz - Gigahertz: 1,000 MHz-one billion Hertz.

GIF - Graphic Interchange Format: A format developed in the mid-1980s by CompuServe for use in photo-quality graphics images. Now commonly used everywhere on-line. The filename extension generally given to GIF files is .gif.

Gigabyte: One billion or one thousand million (109) bytes.

Gigahertz (GHz): A unit of frequency equal to one billion hertz (one billion cycles per second).

GIS (Geographical Information System): Computerized method of capturing, storing, checking, integrating, manipulating, analyzing and displaying data correlated to physical locations. GIS software can create and display maps that represent information as several different layers where each layer holds data about a particular kind of feature.

Glass Master: A highly polished glass disc, coated with photoresist and etched by a laser beam, that is used at the start of the compact disc manufacturing process.

Glitch: **1.** A narrow horizontal bar moving vertically through a television picture. **2.** A short duration pulse moving through the video signal at approximately reference black level on a wave-form monitor. **3.** A random error in a computer programme. **4.** Any random, usually short, unexplained malfunction.

Global Positioning System (gps): A US satellite system that lets those on the ground, on the water or in the air determine their position with extreme accuracy using GPS receivers.

Global System for Mobile communications GSM: TDMA-based second generation mobile Cellular Radio technology, originated in Europe but now used in over 100 countries around the world. GSM supports voice, data and text messaging and allows roaming between different networks - which means that GSM users can take their phones with them to many parts of the world. GSM systems currently operate at 800 MHz, 900 MHz, 1800 MHz or 1900 MHz.

GMSK: The method of modulation used by GSM is Gaussian Minimum Shift Keying (GMSK), with a BT value of 0.3 at a gross data rate of 270 kb/s.

GNU - Gnu's Not Unix: A project of the Free Software Foundation to write a free version of the Unix operating system.

Gopher and Gopher Server: An Internet information retrieval system. Software following a simple protocol for tunneling through a TCP/IP Internet, and running errands, especially the retrieval of "documents." This information system is technically known as a Gopher Server and is part of an international network of Gopher Servers. The Gopher concept was created and initially implemented at the University of Minnesota. The software they created has migrated around the Internet and is now serving the public at large. Since its initial conception, many other organizations have contributed software to this effort.

Gopher: A tool used on the Internet which permits users to locate and retrieve information quickly throughout the Internet.

GPRS (General Packet Radio Service): Radio technology with packet-switching protocols used in GSM networks. Considered a 2.5G technology, GPRS can support data transmission rates of between 20 kbps and 30 kbps.

GPS (Global Positioning System): Navigational system that determines the latitude, longitude and altitude above sea level of any point on the earth's surface by comparing radio signals from several satellites.

Grade Of Service (GOS): mGOS is an estimate of customer satisfaction with a particular aspect of service such as noise, echo or blocking. For example the noise grade of service is said to be 95% if, for a specified distribution of noise, 95% of the people judge the service to be good or better. In traffic networks, GOS defines the percentage of calls that receive no service (blocking) or poor service (long delays). GOS measures apply to all aspects of telecommunications networks. In many cases the literature equates GOS only with the probability of a blocked call. When used without further explanation, GOS generally refers to blocking probability.

Graphics: **(1)** Use of the computer for drawing lines under complete programme control. **(2)** The on-line attachment of a vector scope and light pen to the computer, enabling the user and the computer to interact and jointly draw pictures on the face of the scope.

Ground Start: Ground start is a supervisory signal given at certain coin telephones and PBXs by connecting one side of the line to ground.

Groupware: Groupware is an interactive collaboration of workers or students via networked applications on the computer. It provides audio, video conferencing and data sharing among a group of users using the network at the same time.

GSM (Global System for Mobile Communications): European TDMA standard for digital networks that ensures the compatibility of devices used in different countries. GSM-phones sold in the United States, which operate on 1900 MHz, cannot communicate with 900-MHz European GSM units.

GUI - Graphical user Interface: The underlying principle of client/server computing is empowerment of the end-user through the delivery of information services to the desktop. Services are delivered across the network to a graphical user interface where data is massaged, merged, and maximized. GUIs are designed to juggle multiple applications in windows, through icon-driven commands that standardize application usage and optimize the underlying flow of information across the network.

Guided Media: Guided media is media that constrain electromagnetic or acoustic waves within boundaries established by their physical construction. Examples include paired metallic wire cable, coaxial cable, and fiber optic cable.

H

Hacker On the Net: Unlike among the general public, this is not a bad person; it is simply somebody who enjoys stretching hardware and software to their limits. What many people call hackers, net.denizens refer to as crackers.

Half-Duplex: A communications channel over which both transmission and reception are possible but only in one direction at one time; e.g., a two-wire circuit. Handshake: Two modems trying to connect first do this to agree on how to transfer data.

Handoff: Process by which a cellular telephone call is transferred from one cell site to another.

Handover: What occurs when a cell phone used in a car moves out of the range of one cell and needs to connect to the next available cell. The preceding cell then hands over the connection to the stronger cell.

Handset: That portion of the telephone containing the transmitter and receiver which is designed to be hand-held when the telephone is in use.

Handshake: A preliminary exchange of predetermined signals performed by modems and/or terminals and computers to verify that a communications link has been established and data transmission can proceed.

Hard Copy: **1.** Any physical document. **2.** Computer printout on permanent media such as paper.

Hard-Wired: The direct local wiring of a terminal to a computer system. Hardware: Collectively, electronic circuits, components and associated fitting and attachments. The physical parts, components and machinery associated with computation.

Hayes Compatible: Describes modems that are compatible because they respond to the same set of commands as a modem manufactured by Hayes Microcomputer Products. This has become the standard for microcomputer modems.

HDTV: Higher (than normal) definition TV. HDTV is generally defined as a system that offers, as a minimum, certain specific features and characteristics. These are Wide aspect ratio (now agreed as 19:9 or 1.778:1.; effectively doubled horizontal and vertical resolution; absence of encoding/decoding artifacts (requires component operation); and compact disc quality stereo sound. The technology applied to make HDTV transmittable in existing 6 MHz channels is essentially the same as the technology necessary for multichannel operation in those same channels.

Headend: Electronic control center that receives and re-transmits broadcast TV signals or original signals to receiving locations in a cable system or satellite network. A system usually includes antennas, preamplifiers, frequency converters, demodulators, modulators, processors and other related equipment.

Header: The header is control information appended to a segment of user data for control, synchronization, routing and sequencing of a transmitted data packet or frame.

Hearing Carry Over (HCO): A form of TRS where a person with a speech disability is able to listen to the other end user and, in reply, a Communications Assistant speaks the text as typed by the person with the speech disability.

Hearing Designation Order (HDO): A Commission term, a Hearing Designation Order institutes a comparative or other adjudicatory hearing proceeding, usually before an Administrative Law Judge.

Helical Recording Format: A recording format in which the tape is unwrapped around a cylindrical scanning assembly with one or more recording heads.

Hertz (Hz): Hertz is the measurement that distinguishes electromagnetic waveform energy; number of cycles, or complete waves, that pass a reference point per second; measurement of frequency, by which one hertz equals one cycle per second.

HFC (Hybrid-Fiber Coaxial): Combination of fiber optics and conventional coaxial cable that supports residential two-way, high-speed data access.

HFS - Hierarchical File System: Used on the Macintosh platform for directory structure. The hierarchical directory structure allows a volume to be divided into smaller units known as directories and, in turn, sub-directories. The hierarchical directory structure uses a graphical metaphor of folders containing files or additional folders. Macintosh interface elements, like color icons, are embedded with file structure information.

Hierarchical network: **(1)** A system, in which processing and control functions are performed at designated levels by computers specifically designed for those functions. **(2)** A switching architecture arranged in classes of offices with defined levels of responsibility.

Hierarchy: The relationship of various accounts or entities within a multi-level structure.

High Band: That portion of the electromagnetic spectrum from 174 to 216 MHz, where television channels 7 through 13 are located.

High Definition Television (HDTV): An improved television system which provides approximately twice the vertical and horizontal resolution of the existing television standards. It also provides video quality approaching that of 35 mm film, and audio quality equal to that of compact discs.

High Performance Routing: Dynamically controlled routing within the national long distance network of the owner companies of the Stentor Alliance.

High Sierra Format: The original format proposed by the High Sierra Group for organizing files and directories on CD-ROM. A revised version of this format was adopted by the International Standards Organization as ISO 9660.

High Sierra Group: An ad hoc group of CD-ROM researchers and developers who first gathered at the High Sierra Hotel in Lake Tahoe, CA, to propose a standard CD-ROM file format. This proposal was later amended and approved as the ISO 9660 standard for CD-ROM.

High speed: Refers to data communications systems operating at speeds above 9,600 bits per second.

Hit-on-the-line: Description of the errors caused by external interference such as impulse noise caused by lightning.

Holding Time: The total period a communications channel or facility is in use for each transmission, including both message and operating times.

Hollywood Syndrome: Tendency to base ones video behavior on a model that includes a highly polished presentation rather than interaction and the use of fast-paced visuals for effect rather than substance.

Holy War: Arguments on the Internet that involve certain basic tenets of faith, about which one cannot disagree without setting one of these off. For example: IBM PCs are inherently superior to Macintoshes or Macs are inherently superior to IBMs.

Home Page: The first screen page a user sees when visiting a World Wide Web site.

Home Satellite Dish (HSD): A home receiver that permits the consumer to receive existing satellite transmissions.

Homes Passed: The number of living units passed by cable television distribution facilities in a given cable system service area.

Homing: **(1)** Returning to the starting position, as in a rotary stepping switch. **(2)** Fixing a signal on the originating equipment to determine service quality or problems.

Homogeneous Network: A network of similar host computers such as those of one model of one manufacturer.

Hookswitch: The device on which the telephone receiver hangs or rests when not in use.

Horizontal Blanking: The blanking signal at the end of each scanning line that permits the return of the electron beam from the right to the left side of the raster after the scanning of one line.

Horizontal Consentration: The share of consumers subscribing to a commonly owned system.

Horizontal Resolution: The maximum number of black and white vertical lines that can be resolved within a horizontal expanse of raster equal to one picture height. NTSC television pictures normally have 300 lines of resolution or less.

Horizontal Retrace: The return of the electron beam from the right to the left side of the raster after the scanning of one line.

Horizontal Wiring: In a premises distribution system, horizontal wiring is the connection between the telecommunications outlet in work areas and the telecommunications closet.

Host System: A public-access site; provides Internet access to people outside the research and government community.

Host: Your Internet access provider's computer. You may use one of its hard-wired terminals, if you are at an institution with a mainframe computer connected directly to the Internet, or you may dial up via modem to connect with the Internet access provider's host computer.

Housekeeping Operation: The execution of a computer programme that doesn't directly contribute to a product or service but is essential to the running of the system. For example, the initialization of storage areas or the execution of a calling sequence.

HTML - HyperText Markup Language: The language used to mark up text files with links for use with World Wide Web browsers. This is a file format, based on SGML, for hypertext documents on the Internet. It is very simple and allows for the embedding of images, sounds, video streams, form fields and simple text formatting. References to other objects are embedded using uniform resource locators (URLs).

HTTP (Hyper Text Transfer Protocol): Protocol that tells the server what information to send to a client using a Web browser to view Web pages.

Hub: A designated Wire Center at which bridging, multiplexing or connections to other services are performed. Hub: In local area networks (LANs), a hub is a wiring concentrator equipment used in hierarchical star physical wiring topologies. Those directly connected to terminals or other user devices are of ten referred to as local hubs or concentrators. Central hubs are those at the highest hierarchical level.

Hue: The attribute of color perception that determines whether the color is red, yellow, green, blue, purple, etc.

Hunting: **(1)** Automatic routing of calls to an idle circuit in a prearranged group when the circuit called is busy. **(2)** The movement of a call as it progresses through a group of lines.

Hybrid Carrier: A reseller that owns portions of its network and leases others from other telephone companies and other interexchange carriers.

Hyperlink: Internet term for a word, group of words or graphic that a user clicks a mouse button on. The user is taken to a related piece of information on the network.

Hypermedia: Software that allows the user to interactively manipulate text, images, animation, graphics, sounds, digitized voice, and video.

Hyper-Text Mark-Up Language (HTML): Hyper-Text Mark-up Language is the programming language used to design and present computer sites on the Internet in a graphical user interface fashion. HTML is the language used by programmers to design a Home Page for computers on the Internet as part of the World Wide Web project.

Hyper-Text Transport Protocol (HTTP): The method for moving "hypertext" files across the Internet. Requires an HTTP programme at one end and a server at the other.

Hytelnet: Stands for HyperTelnet. Hytelnet is essentially a database of Telnet sites and other Internet resources that can link to other programmes when you want to connect to a site you've found. Not as useful as Gopher. A system that provides access to libraries around the world through the Internet.

Hz - Hertz: Basic measure of frequency with which an electromagnetic wave completes a full cycle from its positive to its negative pole and back again. Hertz is a unit of frequency equal to one cycle per second. Normal house current is 60 Hertz (60 cycles per second).

I

Icon: A pictorial, symbolic representation of a function or task. Used in GUIs (Graphical User Interfaces) such as Windows and Apple Macintosh Finder.

I-mode: Japanese-developed packet-based information service for mobile phones that allows information and e-mail to be delivered to the user.

Impairments: Impairments is the (e.g., transmission channel and signal impairments) degradation caused by practical limitations of channels, (e.g., signal level loss or attenuation, echo, various types of signal distortion, etc.) or interference induced from outside the channel (such as power-line hum or interference from heavy electrical machinery). The measurement of transmission impairments is an important aspect of predicting whether or not telecommunications systems will sustain the business applications they are intended to support. Signal-to-noise ratio, percent distortion, frequency response, and echo are measurements that define impairments most noticeable by users in analog voice systems.

In-band signaling: **(1)** A type of transmission using an alternate current (AC) signal (usually 2,600 Hz) within the normal voice band. **(2)** An audible signal transmitted end-to-end on a long voice circuit without intermediate signaling equipment; requires that signaling equipment be arranged for "tone on when idle" operation.

Inbound Signaling: Inbound signaling uses not only the same channel path as the voice traffic, but the same frequency range (band) used for the voice traffic.

Inbound Telemarketing: Any incoming sales or service function in an organization. [Inbound telemarketing is found in the following departments: customer service, order entry, reservation sales, technical hotlines or sales support.]

Inbound: The direction of a signal relative to the hub of a local area network (LAN) or other telecommunications system. Inbound signals would be traveling from originating points other than the primary hub in the reverse direction to the hub.

Incumbent Local Exchange Carrier (ILEC): The companies originally franchised under the auspices of the state Public Utilities Commission as the sole provider of local telephone service within a specific geographic area. This includes both Regional Bell Operating Companies (RBOCs) and independent telephone companies.

Independent Telephone Company (ITC): ITC is a local exchange carrier that is not one of the 22 divested Bell-operating companies. ITCs are not generally subject to the restrictions of the MFJ, although some of the larger ones are bound by separate consent decrees. Southern New England Telephone and Cincinnati Bell are generally considered ITCs from a regulatory point of view.

Info Pro(TM): A division of Bell Canada which acts as the company's consulting agent by marketing Bell expertise throughout Canada.

Information Agent: A software programme (currently only an interface to frequently updated databases) that can search numerous databases for information that interests you without your having to know what it is searching. Archie and Veronica are current examples of information agents.

Information Highway: A network, consisting of many connected networks, which has the capacity to carry high-speed, broadband services, including interactive and voice, data, image and video communication. The network will allow customers to reach offices, homes, schools, hospitals and a variety of other institutions.

Information Superhighway: A term describing a network of integrated telecommunications systems connecting people around the world to information, businesses, governments and each other.

Infotainment: The integration of information, education and entertainment services.

Infrared: That portion of the electromagnetic spectrum just below visible light; infrared radiation has a wavelength from 800 nm to about 1mm. Fiber-optic transmission is predominantly in the near-infrared region, about 800 to 1600 nm.

Initialization: The process carried out at the commencement of a programme to test that all indicators and constants are set to prescribed conditions.

Initialize: To set counters, switches, addresses or contents of storage to zero or another starting value at the beginning of or at prescribed points in the operation of a computer routine.

Input Selector Switch (A/B Switches): A switch used by cable customers to alternate between cable and over-the-air television reception through a cable box.

Input/output (I/O channel): A general term for equipment used to communicate with a computer. (2) The process of transmitting information from an external source to the computer, or from the computer to an external source. (3) Buffer area for the temporary storage of data.

Inside Plant: Portion of the telephone network located inside a building; everything in a telephone company central office.

Inside Telephone Wiring: Telephone wiring: For a residence, the wiring usually starts where the line enters the house. It's called the demarcation line. For businesses, the location of the demarcation point varies.

Inside Wiring: Communications wiring that begins at the company's demarcation point and extends to the individual units.

Instructional Design: The methodology used to deliver information in a manner that achieves learning.

Instructional Television Fixed Service (ITFS): A service provided by one or more fixed microwave stations operated by an educational organization and used mainly to transmit instructional, cultural and other educational information to fixed receiving stations.

Integrated Building Distribution Network (IBDN): A universal cable system that provides voice/data within a building (e.g., key, PBX and Centrex telephone systems can be connected to one cabling system).

Integrated Circuit (IC): An electronic component which is used in most computers and other telecommunications equipment to reduce size and increase speed, capability and reliability.

Integrated Services Digital Network (ISDN): A switched network providing end-to-end digital connectivity for the simultaneous transmission of voice, data, video, imaging and fax over several multiplexed communications channels. Employs high-speed, out-of-band signaling protocols that conform to international standards. [Since signaling and communications are separate, the configuration reduces network blockage and provides faster connectivity for users.]

Integrated System: A system in which all components including the various types of amplifiers and taps have been designed from a well-founded overall engineering concept, to be fully compatible with each other.

Intelsat: The International Telecommunications Satellite Organization operates a network of satellites for international transmissions. The stated purpose is the design, development, construction, establishment, maintenance, and operation of the space segment of the global communications satellite system. Interactive: Any application that allows the participants at distant locations to communicate with each other; may indicate two-way video and two-way audio; one-way video and two-way audio through a normal telephone call placed to the origination site; asynchronously (not in real time) as through computer conferencing such as an electronic mail system; or through interaction with a teaching machine such as a computer which is programmed to respond to the user with messages on the screen, voice or other sounds to indicate that an answer is right or wrong.

Interactive Cable System: A two-way cable system that has the capability to provide a subscriber with the ability to enter commands or responses on an in-home terminal and generate responses or stimuli at a remote location. An example of an interactive system would be order entry for Pay-Per-View the order information is transmitted upstream on the cable from the subscriber's terminal to the headend, processed by a billing/authorization computer, and authorization to view a specific Pay-Per-View event is sent downstream to the subscriber's terminal.

Interactive Manual: A Windows-based modem control and diagnostic programme bundled free with each Option 2-in-1 modem. Here you can alter all Hayes AT commands using icons! Just click on the appropriate icon, and the Interactive Manual will instantly alter the modem's settings. You can also change the modem's settings to conform to the PTT specifications of different countries.

Interactive Multimedia: A multi-level multimedia presentation that allows you to access information randomly and nonsequentially.

Interactive Television: Lets owners of ordinary TVs order movies, home shopping, mutimedia packages and other digitized products from electronic jukeboxes.

Interactive Video Data Service (IVDS): A communication system, operating over a short distance, that allows nearly instantaneous two-way responses by using a hand-held device at a fixed location. Viewer participation in game shows, distance learning and E-mail on computer networks are examples.

Interactive Video: The capability to transmit and receive two-way video transmissions between two or more sites.

Interactive Voice Response System (IVR): Automated voice response system to guide callers through a series of routine steps. For example, voice mail prompts you to leave a message or the monetary balance on a pre-paid calling card.

Intercept: To stop a telephone call placed to an improper number and redirect that call to an operator or a recording.

Interchangeable numbering plan area (INPA): A long distance dialing plan in which customers must dial the area code when placing a long distance call - even for calls placed within their own area code.

Interconnect: **(1)** Arrangement that permits the connection of customers telecommunications equipment to a common carrier network. **(2)** Industry name for manufacturers, excluding AT&T and Bell companies, who provide telephone premises equipment.

Interconnection: Equal access to networks between incumbent and competitive local exchange carriers; connecting one network to another, such as a cellular carrier's network, with the local exchange.

Interexchange (IX): Services or channels furnished between one or more rate centers or local and long distance carriers.

Interexchange Carrier (IXC): A company that owns its own transmission facilities and provides telecommunications services between exchanges that are not in the same toll-free calling area. Bell Canada and Unitel Communications Inc. are both interexchange carriers.

Interexchange Mileage: The airline mileage between two cities.

Interexchange Plant: The facilities between the originating switching center and another switching center.

Interexchange voice grade channel; IXVG channel: An analogue-dedicated channel between two exchanges primarily for the use of business customers.

Interexchange: Communication between two different LATAs.

Interface: The link between two pieces of disparate equipment, such as a CPU and a peripheral device. Also, a method of translating data from computer to user. For Internet, the user interface is difficult for the uninitiated to use. Software programmes have been written which change the look of the screen by provide pull-down menus, buttons, hierarchical files folders or hypertext to use and move around the Internet. Software programme names include Mosaic, Lynx, Internet in a Box and GINA.

Interference: **(1)** Unwanted noise, crosstalk or signal deviations on communications channels that result from natural or man-made occurrences. **(2)** Anything not properly a part of the signal or call being transmitted.

Inter-Floor Cabling: Wiring that connects operations on multiple floors but is not part of the public telephone network.

Interlaced Video: Process of scanning video frames in two passes, with each pass painting every other line of the frame onto the screen. NTSC's 525-line frame scans in two fields of 262.5 lines each that take 1/60 second to paint, a frame takes 1/30 second to paint. Noninterlaced video scans complete video frames in one pass usually producing a higher image quality.

Inter-LATA Services: Inter-LATA services are revenues, functions, etc., that relate to telecommunications originating in one LATA and terminating outside that LATA. An interexchange carrier (IXC) is a company which provides telecommunications services between LATAs. (the domain of IXCs).

Interleave: The ability of SONET to mix together and transport different types of input signals in an efficient manner, thus allowing higher-transmission rates.

Intermachine trunk (IMT): Circuit which connects two automatic switching centers.

Intermediate Cross Connects: In a premises distribution system, intermediate cross connects are cross-connects located telecommunications closets.

International Organization for Standardization (ISO): ISO is a worldwide federation of national standards bodies. The work of preparing international standards is normally carried out through ISO technical committees. Draft proposals for international standards adopted by the technical committees are circulated to the National Bodies for approval before their acceptance as Draft International Standards by the committee.

International Record Carrier (IRC): A common carrier engaged in providing overseas telecommunications service. Services furnished traditionally include telex, private line service and alternate voice data service.

International Shortwave Broadcast Station: A station that sends programmes overseas either for direct reception by listeners abroad or for intermediate reception by overseas relay stations that rebroadcast the programmes on shortwave or medium wave stations to nearby audiences.

International Telecommunication Union - ITU: Organization composed of the telecommunications administrations of the participating nations. Focus is the maintenance and extension of international cooperation for improving telecommunications development and applications.

International Telecommunications Satellite Organization (INTELSAT): Formed under a multilateral agreement, it is the organization which owns, maintains, and operates the global satellite system used by over 100 participating countries around the world. COMSAT is the U.S. representative to and participant in INTELSAT.

Internet Appliance: Computer designed only for accessing the Internet, and sending and receiving e-mail.

Internet Backbone: Super-fast network, spanning the world from one major metropolitan area to another, provided by a handful of Internet service providers. These companies and organizations use T3 connections running at approximately 45 mbps linked up at specified interconnection points called national access points. Local ISPs connect to this backbone through routers so data can be carried to its destination.

Internet Protocol (IP): Main protocol (i.e., set of rules that formulates the foundation of communication) that controls data flow from one point to the another. It is actually the low-level common denominator of the Internet.

Internet Service Provider (ISP): Point of access to the Internet for small business and individual users. The ISP provides its customers with dial-up access to its router which relays traffic to web servers on the Internet.

Internet Suite of Protocols: The internet suite of protocols is a collection of computer-communication protocols originally developed under DARPA sponsorship, including the transmission control protocol/internet protocol (TCP/IP).

Internet Telephony Service Provider (ITSP): Company that offers its customers the ability to make phone calls over the public Internet.

Internet: A world-wide network of computer networks in which users at any one computer can, if they have permission, get information from any other computer. The idea was conceived by the Advanced Research Projects Agency (ARPA) of the US government in 1969 and was first known as Arpanet. Since then it has been demilitarised and commercialised and augmented by a series of inventions and innovations, not least of which is the web browser invented by a team led by Tim Berners-Lee in 1991 at CERN, the European Laboratory for Particle Physics. This is the basis for the World Wide Web which has been so successful that it is now often confused in popular conversation with the Internet itself.

Internet Architecture Board (IAB) : The coordinating committee for Internet design, engineering and management.

Internet Access Provider (IAP) : Entity that links companies and individuals to the Internet, usually over a T1 or T3 line.

Interoffice Channel: In LEC tariffs, Interoffice Channel is the channel connecting two serving COs (more accurately serving wire centers). In IXC tariffs, the channel connecting two serving IXC POPs, interoffice transmission facilities used to connect LEC switching systems.

Interoffice trunk (IOT): A direct link between local exchange offices.

Interoperability: The seamless (direct) interconnection of distinct networks so that information and data can circulate efficiently in response to customer demands and service requirements.

Interrupt: Stop a process in such a way that it can be resumed.

Intersatellite Link: A message transmission circuit between two communication satellites, as opposed to a circuit between a single satellite and the earth.

Intertoll trunk: A trunk between toll switching offices in different exchanges used to route long distance calls.

Inverse multiplexing: Combining individual low-speed circuits into a single high-bandwidth data stream.

IP (Internet Protocol): Network layer protocol containing addressing and control information so data packets can be routed over the Internet.

IP Address: 32-bit address of Internet sites, usually represented by dotted decimal notation in TCP/IP networks.

IP Centric: A phone system built around an IP network, not a PBX.

IP Next Generation: New version of Internet Protocol being developed by the Internet Engineering Task Force to handle the larger IP addresses required due to the rapid growth of the Internet.

IP Telephony: Also known as Internet Telephony or Voice over IP (VoIP). Use of Internet Protocol to carry and route two-way voice communications. IP Telephony can support telephone to telephone links through suitable adapters but also voice communications from telephone to IP terminal (such as a PC with sound card) or from IP terminal to IP terminal. The technique promises drastically reduced costs to carriers and therefore prices to end users - but it still suffers problems with quality.

Iridium: Motorola's $3 billion worldwide direct cellular project which will enable users to have one worldwide number. This will be accomplished by a system of low earth orbiting satellites (LEOs).

ISDN - Integrated Services Digital Network: A set of standards provide a common architecture for the development and deployment of digitally integrated communications services. A set of standardized customer interfaces and signaling protocols for delivering digital circuit-switched voice/data and packet-switched data services. ISDN is designed to provide standard interfaces to custom premises equipment such as computers, telephones, and facsimile machines through basic rate interface (BRI) to PBXs, host computers, and LANs through primary rate interface (PRI); to the pubic switched network through SS7; and to local packet data terminals and the public packet-switched network through X.25 and X.75/X.75′ packet services.

ISO: The International Standards Organisation, the body responsible for setting world technical standards. It is based in Geneva, Switzerland.

ISO 9660: The international standard for directory structures and file layout on CDROMs, a logical, structural standard compared to the physical standards for manufacturing called the "Yellow Book." This standard specifies, for single sessions, exactly how information is stored on a CD-ROM to be accessible in any CD-ROM drive running on a variety of common operating systems.

ISOC - Internet Society: ISOC is a membership organization that supports the Internet and is the governing body to which IAB reports.

Isochronous Signals: Isochronous Signals are periodic signals in which the time interval that separates any two corresponding significant occurrences or level transitions is always equal to some unit interval or a multiple of that unit interval. For example, in digitized voice signals, ideally voice samples occur isochronously at precisely the sampling interval or frame rate. Packet data signals are not isochronous.

ISP (Internet Service Provider): Entity that provides access for companies and private individuals to the Internet and the World Wide Web. Additional services offered usually include e-mail, sports scores, weather reports and other Internet utilities.

ITFS Antenna System - Instructional Television Fixed Service: Local (up to 25-mile radius) one-way, over-the-air block of TV channels operating at microwave (very high) frequencies reserved for educational purposes; can be received only by TV installations equipped with a converter to change signals back to those used by a TV set. One-way audio and full motion video. The antenna may be omnidirectional or shaped to cover a specific geographic area. In rare instances the ITFS antenna system can be found to be very directional for special repeater applications or to serve a series of co-linear receive sites.

ITU-T: International Telecommunications Union-Telecommunications Standard Sector, an advisory organization that is part of the United Nations' ITU (International Telecommunication Union). It was formerly known as the Consultative Committee for International Telephone and Telegraph.

IVR: The IVR unit answers the call, greets the caller, and guides the caller through possible responses with a series of voice prompts. The desired information is provided via pre-recorded voice fragments (words) or computer-generated speech.

IWU: InterWorking Unit. This is the network "modem" where all the digital to analogue conversions take place within the digital GSM networks

IXC Miles: On a Price Quote, the coordinates of Location A and Location B are used to calculate mileage-dependent line charges.

J

Jack: A connecting device to which a wire or wires of a circuit may be attached and which is arranged for the insertion of a plug.

JANET - Joint Academic Network: JANET is Great Britain's national network. JANET addresses work backwards from normal Internet addresses (largest domain to the smallest). Mot gateways to JANET perform the necessary translations automatically.

Janus Disc: A CD-ROM that contains data tracks in two or more different formats, such as ISO 9660 and HFS

Java Applet: A programme written in Java to run within a Java-compatible web browser, such as HotJava or Netscape Navigator.

Java Platform: The Java Virtual Machine and the Java core classes make up the Java Platform. The Java Platform provides a uniform programming interface to a 100 percent pure Java programme regardless of the underlying operating system. When implemented on a particular operating system, the Java Platform is said to be Java Compatible if it passes the Java Compatibility Kit suite of tests

Java: Java is similar to the C++ computer language that is already used by many programmers, and it is object-oriented so that new applications can be built from preexisting components. It is a compiled language, so that after it is written, it must be run through a compiler to allow computers to understand it. But - only one compiled version is created which can run on many different platforms. Java can be used to tap into and "mine" databases or create interactive multimedia applications. A common use of Java is to create a news ticker broadcasting the latest news that people can click on to get more details.

Jeopardy: A condition that endangers the completion of scheduled provisioning processes, e.g., no facilities available.

Jitter: **(1)** A distortion caused by the variation of a signal from its references which can cause data transmission errors, particularly at high speeds. **(2)** Variations in amplitude, time, frequency or phase.

JPEG - Joint Photographic Expert Group: JPEG is an industry standard for stillimage compression that is moving into full-motion video. Storing the video signal is a problem as it takes a 300 megabyte hard disk to store just 10 seconds of digital video. Compression is the answer to storage problems. JPEG is a compression technique based upon intraframe encoding technology. It allows full restoration of symmetrically compressed images. Symmetrical compression means that the image takes an equally long time to be compressed as it does to be decompressed. An asymmetrical scheme takes longer to compress an image than to decompress it and typically compresses the image on a computer other than the one to be used for decompression.

Jukebox: CD-ROM drive with a disc changing mechanism, capable of playing multiple discs.

Julian Calendar: Calendar that is used in data processing. The dates are five-digit numbers: the first two digits pertain to the year and the last three to the day of the year (001 through 365 or 366).

Jump Scrolling: Vertical movement (up or down) of data lines, one line at a time, on a cathode ray tube (CRT). Contrast with smooth scrolling.

Justify: **(1)** To position characters of a text so that the left or right margins are aligned. **(2)** To order digits so that the least significant or most significant is always at the left or right margin.

K

Ka-Band: A satellite transmission in the 20 and 30 gigahertz frequency spectrum.

Kbps: Kilobits Per Second a measure of the speed of data capable of passing along a line expressed in thousands of bits.

Kermit: A file transfer protocol named after Kermit the Frog. Kermit is generally slower than XMODEM, YMODEM, and ZMODEM.

Kerning: Reducing the horizontal space between characters of type. Originally, casting a letter so that part of it (e.g., the top of the f) extends beyond the body of the letter, into the space occupied by the next letter. Sometimes used to mean adding or removing space between letters.

Key System : Key telephone system (KTS): In a local environment, terminals and equipment that provide immediate access from all terminals to a variety of telephone services without attendant assistance. Key Systems are generally most appropriate in relatively small business environments, in the range of 50 telephones. Contemporary Electronic Key Telephone Systems (EKTSs), however, often cross the line into the PBX world, providing switching capabilities, as well as impressive functionality and feature content.

Key Telephone System (KTS): KTS is an arrangement of multi-line telephones and associated equipment that permits the station user to depress buttons (keys) to access different central office or PBX lines, as well as to perform other functions. Typical functions include answering or placing a call on a selected line, putting a call on hold, using the intercom feature between phones at the same location, or activating a signal buzzer.

Keyboard: An alphanumeric, input/output, peripheral device used to communicate with a computer.

Killfile: A file that lets you filter Usenet postings to some extent, by excluding messages on certain topics or from certain people.

Kilo: **(1)** Greek word meaning 1000. **(2)** Prefix in the international system of measurements. (Example: kilohertz, kilowatts, etc.)

Kilobaud: The measure of data transmission speed a thousand bits per second.

Kilobit: (Kbps) A measurement for data transmission. One kilobit is 1,000 bits per second.

Kilobyte: A unit of measurement equal to 1024 bytes.

Kilohertz: (kHz) Equals 1,000 hertz (1,000 cycles per second.)

Kine Recording: The technique of converting a video image to motion picture film.

Knowbot: Short for knowledge robot. Embedded machine intelligence capable of automatically and regularly searching for new information on parameters set by the user. At its extreme, the knowbot becomes an intelligent partner in mediating human communication. Sometimes called an agent.

Knowledge Navigator: An information agent popularized by an Apple video about working with computers in the future.

Ku Band: A category of satellite transmissions higher in frequency than those used as "c band" which are being transmitted from satellites placed in the geostationary orbit. The group of microwave frequencies from 12 to 18 GHz and the band of satellite downlink frequencies from 11.7 to 12.2 GHz. The higher frequencies (12 GHz versus 4 GHz) have created the possibility of smaller receive antennas and the realization of direct broadcast satellite (DBS) signals to the end user without the necessity of going through a cable television system or other shared use receive site due to the factors of size and cost.

L

Land Mobile Service: A public or private radio service providing two-way communication, paging and radio signaling on land.

Landline: Fixed line and not mobile. The phone works through a line of wire running through the land to your house and is a fixed line even if you are walking around with the handset. Costs for calling from a land line and a mobile are different.

Large-Scale Integration (LSI) : The process of engraving many thousands of electrical circuits on a small chip of silicon.

Laser - Light Amplification by Stimulated Emission of Radiation: 1. A device for generating coherent electromagnetic signals (e.g., light). Low powered lasers are frequently used to transmit light signals into optical fibers. 2. Laser light contains waves that have the same phase, as opposed to conventional light, whose individual wave phases are unrelated to the phases of the others.

Last Mile: Not meant to be taken literally, this refers to the problems of communications that occur in that "last mile" - from the exchange to the house or final destination. Often the last mile is old, limited bandwidth copper wire that cannot support the faster modems and computers.

Latency: Time it takes a packet to travel from source to destination. Latency and bandwidth define the speed and capacity of a network.

Lavaliere: A small microphone that can be clipped onto clothing or suspended from neck cords and worn in front of the chest.

Layer: (1) Related processes, activities or information that constitute one level in a hierarchy or network platform. (2) Related communications-processing functions that comprise one level in a hierarchy of functions within the OSI reference model.

Learning Curve: A planning technique calculation based on the premise that workers are able to produce any new product more quickly after they get used to making it.

Learning Styles: A learner's learning style is as individual as a fingerprint. We all learn differently. The Canfield Learning Style instrument identifies styles in iconic, direct experience, listening, qualitative, numeric, and other modes. The student-centered approach to learning styles is to have the facilitator adapt his/her style to that which will meet the student's learning style. Since even a small class will present varied learning styles, it is best to prepare materials that use a variety of technology delivery methods so that the needs of all learners are met.

Leased Lines: A term used to describe the leased or rented use of dedicated lines from point to point. Lines could include fiber optic cables, telephone cables, microwave or other transmission systems.

Least Cost Routing (LCR): Method for automatic selection of the least costly facility for transmission of a call.

Letter of Agency (LOA): What the customer can sign to give some other entity additional authority to contact the LEC on their behalf to facilitate the switching of long distance carriers.

Level: (1) A group of related functions, activities or occurrences. (2) Expressed as the relative signal strength at a fixed point in a communications circuit .

Lifeline/Link-Up Services: Programmes that help low-income households to afford local telephone service. Lifeline assists with monthly telephone bills, and Link-Up assists with connection and installation charges.

Light Emitting Diode (LED) : A semiconductor which emits light when a proper voltage is applied to its terminals.

Light Pen: A pen-like device that contains a photosensitive cell and small aperture lens that produces or detects electronic signals; can be used to write free-hand directly on a TV screen or to enter, edit and position computer text or graphics.

Lightwave Communications: The use of light as the primary medium in an actual application. Lightwave communications is sometimes used in place of "optical" to avoid confusion with image transmissions such as facsimile or television.

Lightweight Directory Access Protocol (LDAP): An Internet standard for Internet telephony products that access directory servers.

Limited-distance Modem: (1) A short-haul modem or line driver. Since line conditions can be better controlled over short distances, some limited-distance modems operate at higher speeds than modems that are designed for use over analog telephone facilities.

Line Alarm Indication Signal (AIS-L): AIS-L is generated by Section Terminating Equipment (STE) upon the detection of a Loss of Signal or Loss of Frame defect, on an equipment failure. AIS-L maintains operation of the downstream regenerators, and therefore prevents generation of unnecessary alarms. At the same time, data and orderwire communication is retained between the regenerators and the downstream Line Terminating Equipment (LTE).

Line Conditioning: Adjustment and control of the properties of a leased line to bring its characteristics within specified tariff limits; generally improves the frequency response and delay considerations of the line. [Line conditioning services provided by telephone carriers are designated as Type C or D (example C1, C2 or C4).]

Line Driver: A modem alternative used when transmitting via Electronics Industry Association (EIA) cable over short distances, usually several hundred feet. (2) Device to amplify signals and reshape distorted pulses.

Line Loading: Use of electrical components to improve the response characteristics of a communications line.

Line Overhead (LOH): 18 bytes of overhead accessed, generated, and processed by line terminating equipment. This overhead supports functions such as locating the SPE in the frame, multiplexing or concatenating signals, performance monitoring, automatic protection switching, and line maintenance.

Line Printer: **(1)** A device that prints a line of characters as a unit. (2) A line-at-a-time printer.

Line Remote Defect Indication (RDI-L): A signal returned to the transmitting Line Terminating Equipment (LTE) upon detecting a Loss of Signal, Loss of Frame, or AIS-L defect. RDI-L was previously known as Line FERF.

Line Side: A circuit from a subscriber's telephone to the end or central office.

Line Terminating Equipment (LTE): Network elements such as add/drop multiplexers or digital cross-connect systems which can access, generate, and process Line Overhead.

Line: A communications channel. Also called a circuit, trunk or facility. It often refers to customer access to the public switched telephone network (e.g., residence line, individual business line).

Linear: Video technology designed to be played from beginning to end without stops.

Line-side Access: A type of access in which customers making long distance calls must dial extra digits, in addition to the called party's telephone number.

Link Layer: **(1)** The logical entity in the OSI model relative to transmission of data between adjacent network nodes. **(2)** The second processing level in the OSI model, between the physical and the network layers.

Link: Telecommunications circuit between any two telecommunications devices, not including the equipment connector. It may be a data communications circuit or a direct cable connection.

Lip Sync: Synchronization of the sound portion with the visual portion of a television programme.

Loading Coil: Inductors, added in a series on the phone line, that extends the range of a local loop for voice-grade communications by compensating for the parallel capacitance of the line. They cannot be used on DSL connections.

Local Access and Transport Area (LATA): A contiguous local exchange area which includes every point served by a local phone company within an existing community of interest. It also serves as the dividing line for the allocation of assets and liabilities between AT&T and the Bell Operating Companies. LATAS were established by the Department of Justice as a result of the AT&T divestiture.

Local Access Provider: Any organization that is authorized to provide local access. (May or may not be the LEC.)

Local Access: Local Loop. The connection from a subscriber to the Central Office. The portion of a circuit connecting the LEC's CO with the customer's premise equipment across the local network.

Local Area Network (LAN): LAN is a premises high-speed (typically in the range of 10 Mbps) data communications system wherein all segments of the transmission medium (typically coaxial cable, twisted pair or optical fiber) are contained within an office or campus environment.

Local Automatic Message Accounting (LAMA): An automatic message accounting (AMA) system in which billing data collection equipment is located in local switching centres (local offices). LAMA eliminates routing restrictions, allowing many long distance calls to be routed directly from one local office to another. This results in improved network efficiency because without LAMA, the call would have to be routed through a toll office for billing purposes.

Local Channel: In LEC tariffs, a local channel is the local loop that connects customer premises to serving LEC wire centers. In IXC tariffs, the network components (transmission, switching, other) used to connect customer premises to serving IXC POPs.

Local Distribution Area (LDA): An area that includes the rate centers (NXXs) served by an originating city.

Local Dynamic Routing: Dynamically controlled routing (DCR) within a local calling area.

Local Exchange Carrier (LEC) : The local or regional telephone company that owns and operates lines to customer locations and Class 5 Central Office Switches.

Local Loop Provider (LLP): Company that offers other companies accesses to a telephone switch.

Local Loop: The part of a communications circuit between the subscriber's equipment and the equipment in the local exchange. Also known as the subscriber loop, local line and access line.

Local Measured Service (LMS): A pricing structure for local calls which requires customers to pay according to usage, rather than simply paying a flat monthly fee. LMS generally combines access (fixed rate) and usage (variable rate) charges. The access charge is usually set at a rate substantially less than the prevailing flat rate and may include a usage allowance. Usage charge calculations are typically based on up to four variables: frequency (the number of calls placed); duration (how long calls last); the geographical distance the call covers; and the time of day or week the call was placed.

Local Multipoint Distribution Services (LMDS): Point/multipoint service with two-way capability to transmit voice, data, and other video information. LMDS can offer innovative consumer services such as two-way interactive video, advanced teleconferencing, telemedicine, telecommuting, and high-speed data services.

Local Number Portability (LNP) : The ability to change phone companies without having to change phone numbers.: Local Loop: The communications channel, usually a physical line, between the subscriber's location and his local central office. Also known as the subscriber

Local Rate: These numbers start 084 and will cost you up to 4.5p if you call from a BT land line (a fixed line phone). If you call from your mobile call costs will vary and you may be charged more.

Location - Remote: Production shooting site other than a studio.

Locked Mode: A virtual tributary mode that fixes the starting location of the VT SPE. Locked mode has less pointer processing than floating mode.

Log Off: Disconnect from a host system.

Log On/Log In: Connect to a host system or public-access site.

Long Distance Carrier: A company providing long-distance phone service between LECs and LATAs.

Loop : (1) A closed circuit. **(2)** The single connection from a switching center to an individual telecommunications instrument.

Loop Back: A method of performing transmission tests on a circuit which does not require the assistance of personnel at the distant end.

Loop Charge: The installation and monthly recurring fees charged by the LEC to connect a customer to their long distance carrier via T-1.

Loop Length: Typically, loop length is a complete electrical circuit; the pair of wires that winds its way from the central office to the telephone set or system at the customer's premises.

Loop Signaling: Loop signaling is a method of signaling over dc circuit paths that utilizes the metallic loop formed by the line or trunk conductors and terminating circuits.

Loop Start: Loop start is a supervisory signal given at a telephone or PBX in response to closing the loop's DC current path.

Loop Transmission Facilities: Loop transmission facilities connect switching systems to customer premises equipment throughout the serving area. A loop is a transmission path between a customer's premises and a LEC central office. The most common form of loop, a pair of wires, is also called a line. A loop" can be derived from digital loop carrier (DLC) systems also referred to as subscriber loop carrier (SLC) systems.

Lottery (random selection): An alternative method to auctions and comparative hearings for allocating spectrum space to competing applicants in various services. In a lottery, the winning applicant is chosen at random. A message transmission circuit between two communication satellites, as opposed to a circuit between a single satellite and the earth.

Lotus: Famous for the Lotus 1-2-3 spreadsheet of the 1980's, and more recently for it's Notes Groupware system. Bought by IBM in 1995.

Low Band: That portion of the electromagnetic spectrum from 54 to 88 MHz, where television channels 2-6 are located.

Low Earth Orbiting Satellite - LEO: Low earth orbit satellites which require 77 small, smart satellites to provide linkage around the world. The satellites move overhead in their low orbit. Motorola's Iridium (from the element Iridium which has 77 electrons) uses the concept to provide, digital, satellite-based personal communications via small, handheld transportable receivers. With the system, voice, fax, or data calls can be made or received anywhere. The user will have one universal telephone number for the phone.

Low Noise Amplifier (LNA) : Located at the antenna. Refers to electronic equipment, used in conjunction with satellite reception, intended to amplify extremely weak satellite signals without introduction of noise. They are rated in different noise temperatures, expressed in degrees Kelvin. The lower the noise temperature figure, the higher the carrier-to-noise ratio, and the better the picture.

Low Power fm Radio (lpfm): A broadcast service that permits the licensing of 50-100 watt FM radio stations within a service radius of up to 3.5 miles and 1-10 watt FM radio stations within a service radius of 1 to 2 miles.

Low Power Television Service (LPTV): A broadcast service that permits programme origination, subscription service, or both via low powered television translators. Low Power Television service includes the existing translator service and operates on a secondary basis to regular television stations. Transmitter output is limited to 1000 watts for a UHF station, 10 watts for a normal VHF station, and 100 watts when VHF operation is on an allocated channel.

Low Speed: Data communications systems operating at speeds of less than 2,400 bits per second (bps).

Luminance: **1.** Luminous flux emitted, rejected, or transmitted per unit of solid angle per projected area of the source. **2.** The photometric equivalent of brightness. 3. The brightness part of a television picture.

Lux: Unit of n equal to 1 lumen per square meter or approximately 0.1 candle power.

M

MacBinary: A file format that combines the three parts of a Macintosh file; the data fork, the resource fork, and the Finder information block. No other computers understand the normal Macintosh file format, but they can transmit the MacBinary format without losing data. When you download a binary Macintosh file from another computer using the MacBinary format, your communications programme automatically reassemble the file into a normal Macintosh file.

Machine Language: Binary code that can be directly executed by the processor, as opposed to assembly or high-level language.

MacTCP: A Control Panel from Apple that implements TCP on the Macintosh. MacTCP is required to use programmes such as Fetch and TurboGopher.

Magnetic Media: Any medium on which data is stored as variations in magnetic polarity. Usually floppy disks, hard disks, and tape.

Magnetic Tape: A mylar tape, coated with magnetic particles, on which audio, video or data can be stored.

Magneto-optical: An information storage medium that is magnetically-sensitive only at high temperatures. A laser heats a small spot, which allows a magnet to change its polarity. The medium is stable at normal temperatures. Magneto-optical discs can be erased and re-recorded.

Mailing List: Essentially a conference in which messages are delivered right to your mailbox, instead of to a Usenet newsgroup. You get on these by sending a message to a specific e- mail address, which is often that of a computer that automates the process.

Main Cross-Connects: In a premises distribution system, main cross-connects are the cross connects located in an equipment room.

Main Distribution Frame (MDF): A steel bar framework that is the major cross connect point for COs and TOCs. Used to interconnect loop cable pairs and line equipment terminals on a switching system.

Main pbx: A small, local telephone office or a device with the same functionality directly connected to a tandem switch via an access trunk group.

Major Trading Area (MTA): Boundaries that segment the country for telecommunication licensing purposes. MTAs are based on Rand McNally's Commercial Atlas & Marketing Guide. Each MTA is named after one or more cities which are Major Trading Centers. MTAs are larger than BTAs. The FCC has used MTAs to license a number of services, including broadband and narrowband PCS.

Manual Tie Line: A private communication channel which requires the assistance of an attendant at both ends of the circuit in order to complete a call.

Map/Demap: A term for multiplexing, implying more visibility inside the resultant multiplexed bit stream than available with conventional asynchronous techniques.

Mapping: The process of associating each bit transmitted by a service into the SONET payload structure that carries the service. For example, mapping a DS1 service into a SONET VT1.5 associates each bit of the DS1 with a location in the VT1.5.

Mark: **(1)** Symbol or symbols that indicate the beginning or the end of a field, word, item of data or sets of data such as a file, a record or a block. **(2)** To place a lead or ground on a terminal so that a hunting circuit may find that position and connect other equipment to it. **(3)** An indication, often in software, which shows the class of service to which a line is entitled, such as residential, business or public coin phone.

Market Sustainable Rate of Contribution: The level of contribution which leads to the highest sustainable contribution revenue over the long run (i.e., the level above which there would be a net revenue loss due to market forces, such as bypass).

Market-driven Local Service Pricing Mechanisms: Refers to the setting of local prices based on the interaction between customers and suppliers in a competitive market place, recognizing regulatory constraints.

Master Antenna Television System (MATV): An antenna system that serves a concentration of TV sets such as in an apartment building or hotel. MATV utilizes one central antenna to pick up broadcast signals.

Master Control: Nerve center for telecasts. Controls the programme input, switching, and retrieval for on-the-air telecasts.

Master: The original video tape, audio tape or film of a finished product. Usually stored in a vault or area protected from the environment. Dubs are made from the master. Once the master is worn out, it can not be replicated.

Mastering Facility: A manufacturing plant where compact disc "masters" are created for the mass production or replication of the actual compact discs.

Matte Key: Keyed (electronically cut-in) title whose letters are filled with shades of gray or a specific color.

Matte: The keying of two scenes; the electronic laying in of a background image behind a foreground scene, such as a picture of a town meeting behind the newscaster reporting on the meeting.

MATV - Master Antenna Television: Centrally-located receiving system that distributes off-air signals and to multiple places in the cable transmission system.

MBONE - Multicast Backbone: Internet. An outgrowth of the first two IETF "audiocast" experiments in which live audio and video were multicast from the IETF meeting site to destinations around the world. The idea is to construct a semi-permanent IP multicast testbed to carry the IETF transmissions and support continued experimentation between meetings. The MBONE is a virtual network. It is layered on top of portions of the physical Internet to support routing of IP multicast packets since that function has not yet been integrated into many production routers. The network is composed of islands that can directly support IP multicast, such as multicast LANs like Ethernet, linked by virtual point-to-point links called "tunnels". The tunnel endpoints are typically workstation-class machines having operating system support for IP multicast and running the "mrouted" multicast routing daemon.

MCC - Microelectronics and Computer Technology Corporation: An industry consortium that developed the MacWAIS software.

MCU - Multipoint Control Unit: MCU's have the ability to support multipoint videoconferences on codecs of the same brand and (in most cases) model.

MDF (Main Distribution Frame): Connection arrangement between internal lines and telephones wires coming from outside. The central office main frame is the termination point for outside plant wiring.

MDS: Pay television delivery service relayed by microwave to small dish antennas.

Mean Time Between Failure - (MTTR): The average time required to restore a customer's service after a network failure.

Media Player: A media player is a piece of application software for playing back multimedia files. Most media players support an array of media formats, including both audio and video files.

MediaLinx Interactive Inc.: A new company created by Bell Canada and its Stentor partners as part of their Beacon initiative for the information highway. Launched in October 1994, MediaLinx Interactive Inc. will seek and develop interactive and multimedia services and applications.

Medium Speed: Refers to data communications systems operating at and above 2,400 bits per second up to the speed limit obtainable on a voice grade channel (i.e., 9,600 bps).

Medium: (1) Material on which computer data is recorded, for example, magnetic tape, floppy diskette. **(2)** Any material substance that can be used for the propagation of signals from one point to another. **(3)** The communications forum chosen on marketing promotions and/or customer information.

Meet-Me Bridge - Meet-Me Teleconferencing: A type of telephone bridge that can be accessed directly by calling a certain access number; provides dial-in teleconferencing. The term "meet-me bridging" refers to the use of this type of bridge.

Mega: 1. Ten to the sixth power, 1,000,000 in decimal notation. **2.** When referring to storage capacity, two to the twentieth power, 1,048,576 in decimal notation.

Megabits Per Second (Mbps): A measure of the speed of data capable of passing along a line expressed in millions of bits.

Megabyte: A unit of measurement equal to 1024 x 1024 bytes, or 1024 kilobytes; 8 million bits.

MegaHertz - MHz: One million cycles per second.

Member: At the FCC, the term "member" refers to a Commissioner.

Memory: Computer's information storage capability. RAM - random access memory;

Menu: A list of symbols and functions that can be selected on a computer system.

Mesochronous: A network whereby all nodes are timed to a single clock source, thus all timing is exactly the same (truly synchronous).

Message Retrieval: The capability to retrieve a message at the time it has entered an information system.

Message Telephone System (MTS): (1) Generic name for the switched long distance service offered by all interexchange carriers. **(2)** An offering for which a charge is made in accordance with a measured amount of usage referred to as message units. Also referred to as Measured Telephone Service or Direct Distance Dialing (DDD).

Message Toll Service - MTS: Pay-by-the-minute switched long distance services. Includes conventional long distance and measured WATS.

Message Unit (MU): Standard against which charges for messages based on time and distance are measured.

Message: Complete transmission of data or text. Sometimes used interchangeably with block.

Metal Master: A metal disc created by plating an etched glass master disc with nickel. Used in a mastering facility to create metal stampers for the mass production of compact discs.

MHz - Megahertz: Refers to a frequency equal to one million Hertz, or cycles per second.

Microcomputer: A relatively precise term for computers whose central processing units (CPUs) are microprocessor chips. By contrast, mainframes and most minicomputers have CPUs containing large circuitry. Microcomputers include personal computers, small business computers, desktop computers, and home computers.

Microfiche: A system of storing and retrieving information microforms, consisting of film in the form of separate sheets, that contain original text, pictures, data, or anything which has been reduced to micro- images for a greater storage efficiency and arranged in a grid pattern for location of those original images by means of Cartesian coordinates.

Microfilm: A system of storing and retrieving information microforms, consisting of film as a data medium, usually in the form of a roll or strip, that contains micro-images of the original information. The images are generally in a sequential arrangement rather than in rows or columns as on microfiche.

Microprocessor: The heart of the computer. This is a silicon chip with the computer's central processing unit implemented on the chip.

Microsecond: One millionth of a second.

Microsoft : The world's largest developer and publisher of software based in Redmond, Seattle, USA. Headed by William (Bill) Gates, the richest (non-royal) person on this planet.

Microsoft Windows: A GUI (graphic user interface) operating environment developed by Microsoft for use on PCs running under the MS-DOS operating system.

Microwave Band: Those frequencies from about 1 gigahertz upward that use microwave frequencies for point-to-point and point-to-multipoint communications, including common carriers, cable TV operators, broadcasters, and private operational fixed users.

Microwave System: A high-capacity transmission system that transmits information via high-frequency radio signals called microwaves. Initially, microwave systems offered analogue transmission. Current systems offer digital transmission and complement fiber optic transmission systems.

Microwave: That portion of the electromagnetic spectrum from approximately 1,000 Megahertz to 100,000 Megahertz. The microwave energy is capable of being focused in concentrated beams in specific directions due to its short wavelength characteristics and sent over long distances. Point-to-point transmission system that transmit signals through the air using transmitters and antennas attached to tall towers. Provides programme audio and video plus the capacity for additional voice and data material. It is also capable of being transmitted over wide areas from a central point or shaped into specific coverage areas with special antennas (ITFS). Extreme examples of long distance focused microwave transmissions are the signals sent from a satellite uplink earth station to a satellite 22,300 miles above the earth and from that satellite back to earth.

Midband: The band of cable television channels A through I, lying between 120 and 174 MHz.

MIDI - Musical Instrument Digital Interface: **1.** An industry-standard connection for computer control of musical instruments and devices. **2.** Musical Instrument Digital Interface. Industry standard for exchange of musical information between computers and musical instruments or music synthesizers.

Midsplit System: A cable-based communications system that enables signals to travel in two direction, forward and reverse simultaneously with upstream (reverse) transmission from 5 MHz to about 100 MHz and downstream (forward) transmission greater than about 150 MHz. Exact crossover frequencies vary from manufacturer to manufacturer.

MIME - Multipurpose Internet Mail Extensions: A new Internet standard for transferring non-textual data, such as audio messages or pictures, via e-mail.

Minicomputer: An intermediate range computer, between full-size mainframes and 16-bit microcomputers. Historically, minicomputers have served dedicated uses, such as in scientific and laboratory work.

Misroute: A condition that results in the 9-1-1 call going to the wrong PSAP. A call can be misrouted if the emergency service number and associated routing information are incorrect in the E9-1-1 database and/or tandem database. A call can also be misrouted if the call is an ANI failure, which automatically default routes.

Mixed Mode Disc: A CD-ROM that contains both CD-ROM (Yellow Book) and CDAudio(Red Book) tracks.

MMS: Multimedia messages/photo messages. This enables you to take pictures and videos on your mobile phone and then send and receive them.

MNP: Microcom Networking Protocol. Error control and data compression techniques, created by Microcom, that many newer modems use. They are built into the modem, unlike software error correction in file transfer protocols. There are different MNP levels. Levels 1-4 are error control protocols, and level 5 is a data compression protocol that can compress data to about 50% of its original size. A modem with MNP-5 also has MNP-4. MNP 1-4 is also included in the ITU V.42 error correction system.

Mobile Communications: A wireless form of communication in which voice and data information is emitted, transmitted and received via microwaves. This type of communication allows individuals to converse with one another and/or transmit and receive data while moving from place to place. Some examples include: cellular and digital cordless telephones; pagers; telephone answering devices; air-to-ground telecommunications; and satellite-based communications.

Mobile Telephone Switching Office (MTSO): Central computer that connects a wireless phone call to the public telephone network. The MTSO also handles call monitoring, billing and handoffs.

Modem: A MOdulator DEModulator computer peripheral which allows a computer to communicate over telephone lines. This is the heart of computer telecommunications. The main factor that differentiates modems is their speed, measured in bps. Analogue modems talk to one another by converting digital info from the computer into tones called PSK's. An ordinary analogue modem cannot be physically connected to a GSM phone because networks will not carry PSK tones.

Modification Of Final Judgment (MFJ): MFJ is a ruling issued by U.S. District Court Judge Harold Greene which concluded the U. S. Justice Department's antitrust suit against AT&T by modification of an earlier (1956) consent decree's final judgment.

Modular: Constructed with standardized units or dimensions for flexibility and variety in use; allows for easy replacement, substitution, expansion or reconfiguration of modules or sub-assemblies.

Modulation: A process whereby a signal is transformed from its original form into a signal that is more suitable for transmission over the medium between transmitter and receiver.

Modulator: A device which converts the video signal and audio signal onto a viewable TV channel. It takes the video and audio signals that are separated by the receiver and combines them into a signal that can be received by an ordinary TV set. This signal is called an "RF" signal, meaning radio frequency, and is usually set for either channel 3 or 4. The advantage of using a modulator is that it permits the use of standard TV receivers for displays, but the signal quality is not as good as using a direct video and audio feed to a monitor TV display. As with receivers, modulators should also be redundant.

Module: **(1)** A unit of something. **(2)** A unit of code performing a distinct function.

Monitor: A television monitor is capable of projecting from an attached device such as a video tape recorder or camera; or from a cable such as that connected by cable companies or the cable from the satellite receiving unit. It is not equipped with receiver electronics which enable it to receive local broadcast channels.

Monitoring Device: Equipment which records data - originating number, length, location - on calls placed through a company telephone system.

Mosaic: A free graphical front end to the Internet that supports browsing of multimedia data that includes plain and formatted text, picture, video and sound. The data is based on the hypertext document format where text or pictures can act as links to other places in the same or different documents. Mosaic provides a simple graphical user interface (GUI) that enables easy access to the data stored on the Internet. These data may be simple files or hypertext documents. The document a user points to on the receiving desktop could be on the same machine or on another computer elsewhere on the Internet. Mosaic clients are currently available for Windows, Macintosh, the X Window System and many flavors of UNIX. Mosaic was developed by the National Center for Supercomputing (NCSA).

Most economical route selection (MERS): Method for automatic selection of the least costly facility for transmission of a call.

MOTSS - Members of the Same Sex: Originally an acronym used in the 1980 federal census.

MoU: Memorandum of Understanding, the GSM body that overseas GSM standards and implementation around the world. It comprises operators and some manufacturers.

Mouse: Hand-held device which is moved around on a flat surface in order to position the cursor on a video display.

MP3: MP3 is an acronym for MPEG layer 3, which is a compressed audio format. A compression ratio of up to 12 to 1 compression is possible, which produces high sound quality.

Mpbs: In data transfer, a megabit (nominally 1 million bits but actually1,048,576 bits) per second. When used to describe data storage, a megabit is 1,024 kilobits.

MPC - Multimedia Personal Computer: A standard which describes a PC that can run Microsoft's Windows efficiently because the system software beneath multimedia would be "Windows with Multimedia Extension." The specification calls for added audio and CD-ROM hardware. MPC is a registered trademark of the MPC Marketing Council.

MPEG - Moving Pictures Experts Group: Multimedia compression standard for professional and consumer applications - digital video, digital audio and systems compression. MPEG compression compresses similar frames of video, tracks elements which change between frames and discards the redundant information. This allows fullmotion video to be sent at CD-ROM data rates - around 160kbps. MPEG, which is now being called MPEG1 in some circles achieves increased compression through the use of a combination of interframe and intraframe (sometimes called MPEG 1-Frame) image and audio compression algorithms, including predictive and interpolated technologies. These techniques analyze the degree of motion present in a search range and predict the "temporal redundancy" (anticipated repetitive motion) occurring between adjacent frames. As in JPEG, pixel search blocks form the basis of the representative sampling unit.

MSAG Master Street Address Guide: The MSAG contains all valid streets in the E9-1-1 service area. It includes low/high house numbers (address range), community name and ESN.

MUD/MUSH/MOO/MUCK/DUM/MUSE: These are multi-user, text based, virtual reality games. A MUD (Multi-User Dungeon) is a computer programme which users can log into and explore. Each user takes control of a computerized persona/avatar/incarnation/character. You can walk around, chat with other characters, explore dangerous monster-infested areas, solve puzzles, and even create your very own rooms, descriptions and items. There are an astounding number of variations on the MUD theme.

Multichannel Multipoint Distribution Service (MMDS): A service which uses omnidirectional microwave signals to deliver video programmes to subscribers.

Multidrop Line: Communications link with more than one terminal or station connected to it.

Multi-Frequency signalling (MF): A method of dialling using combinations of tones to denote different numbers. Widely used on PABX's, but now also used between PABX's or DELs and electronic public exchanges. Also known as MF4.

Multileaving: Transmission, usually via bisync facilities and protocols, of a variable number of datastreams between user devices and a computer.

Multiline Telephone: A multiline telephone is a telephone that incorporates visual displays and switches (keys) that permit the station user to access more than one central office or other line and to perform other desired functions. Typical functions include answering or originating a call on a selected line, putting a call on hold, operating an intercom feature, a buzzer, etc. Displays can indicate busy, ringing and message waiting status.

Multi-Link Audio: Any application allowing viewers to be connected by phone (usually by audio bridge) to the spot where the broadcast originates.

Multimedia Extensions: Adds audio and video recording and playback capabilities to Microsoft Windows. Part of the MPC standard.

Multimedia: A rapidly growing communications technology that allows people to communicate via computer using any combination of text, data, voice, graphics, photographs, video and audio simultaneously. Multimedia allows users to send, share, retrieve or create information of almost any kind from their desktop or portable computer.

Multimode Optical Fiber(S): Multimode fibers, with much wider cores than single mode fibers, allow light to enter at various angles, and reflect (bounce off of) core-clad boundaries as electromagnetic (light) wave propagates from transmitter to receiver. From a technical performance trade-off point of view, single mode fiber exhibits bandwidths of up to 100,000 MHz (MHz = 1,000,000 hertz or cycles per second = one megahertz) while multimode band width is in the range of 1,000 to 2,000 MHz (1,000 MHz = one billion hertz = one gigahertz = 1 GHz).

Multimode: Optical fiber that allows more than one mode of light signal transmission. Multimode optical fiber has a core diameter between 50 microns and 62.5 microns (1 micron is 1/1,000th of a inch, or 0.001 inch). Dispersion of light is greater than single-mode fiber, so segments are shorter to reduce attenuation.

Multiple Access: The ability of more than one user to use a transponder. Transponders have three basic resources frequency, time and space. The frequency domain is used in FDMA. Time domain multiple access is used in TDMA by time-sharing the transponder. Space domain multiple access makes use of either the polarization discrimination, orthogonal digital codes or through spread-spectrum techniques.

Multiple Address Systems (MAS): A microwave point-to-multipoint communications system, either one-way or twoway, serving a minimum of four remote stations. The private radio MAS channels are not suitable for providing a communications service to a larger sector of the general public, such as channels the Commission has allocated for cellular, paging, or specialized mobile radio service (SMR).

Multiple Audio Subcarrier Tuning: Essential to take advantage of radio and data services riding piggy-back on video signals. Also, some programming may use nonstandard frequencies.

Multiple System Operator (MSO): A company that operates more than one cable TV system.

Multiplex: **(1)** To interleave or simultaneously transmit two or more messages on a single channel. **(2)** A communications arrangement where multiple devices share a common transmission channel, though only one may transmit at a time.

Multiplexer: Hardware device that allows handling of multiple variable speed signals over a single, higher speed channel.

Multiplexing: Multiplexing is a technique that enables a number of communications channels to be combined into a single broadband signal and transmitted over a single circuit. At the receiving terminal, demultiplexing of the broadband signal separates and recovers the original channels. Multiplexing makes more efficient use of transmission capacity to achieve a low per channel cost. Two basic multiplexing methods used in telecommunications systems, are frequency division multiplexing (FDM) and time division multiplexing (TDM). multiplexing: Process or equipment that combines data from two or more individual circuits onto a higher speed circuit for transmission.

Multiplexor - MUX: Device that uses one of several techniques to combine multiple analog or digital signals onto a single path.

Multipoint Distripution Service (MDS): Also known as "wireless cable," this is a one-way, domestic public radio service broadcast on microwave frequencies from a fixed station that transmits (usually in an omnidirectional pattern) to multiple receiving facilities located at fixed points determined by the subscriber's location.

Multipoint: **(1)** Line or channel connecting more than two different service points. **(2)** Circuit having points served by three or more switches.

Multiprocessor: A computer employing two or more processing units under integrated control.

Multisession: A drive that has the ability to read a CD-ROM on which data was recorded in at least two different recording sessions, or a disc that contains data recorded at different times.

Multitasking: System that can run two or more programmes at the same time. [Apple's Multifinder, AT&T's UNIX and IBM's OS/2 are multitasking operating systems. By contrast, MS-DOS is a single-tasking operating system.]

Multi-User Dimension (MUD): This term refers to users who connect to each other via a host computer.

Must Carry (retransmission): A term from the 1992 Cable Act, it refers to a cable system's mandatory signal carriage of both commercial and noncommercial television broadcast stations that are "local" to the area served by the cable system.

Mux: [Abbreviation for multiplexing] The process or equipment for combining a number of paths into a single path or bit stream for transmission.

MVNO (Mobile Virtual Network Operator): Company that buys services from carriers and then offers wireless service under a new brand name.

N

Nanosecond (NS, NSEC): One-thousandth-millionth (or billionth) of a second. (10-9 second.).

Narrowband Network: A network capable of carrying voice, video and data signals (e.g., telephone service, electronic mail, paging services and faxes). Technically, a narrowband network is capable of carrying up to 64,000 bits of information per second.

Narrowband: A term applied to telecommunications facilities capable of carrying only voice, facsimile images, slow-scan video images and data transmissions at "kilobit" speeds. The term is commonly applied to voice-grade analog facilities and to digital facilities operating at low speeds.

Narrowcast: Transmission of programmes to a specifically defined audience normally using the newer technology delivery systems. Sometimes referred to as a target audience, a limited audience, or a "narrow" audience, hence the name "narrowcast."

Natural Market: A market in which market forces determine price, technology, investment decisions and the nature of services available.

Net Computers (NC): Small computers with enough memory to navigate the Internet and download content. The Net Computers were created to close the educational gap between children in prosperous and low-income schools - usually called the haves and have-nots. Net computers will work in schools, homes, small business and other sites.

Net: The Net-sanctioned way to refer to the Internet for the initiated.

Netiquette: Network + etiquette= netiquette. Customs and socially accepted behavior for using the Internet networks.

Network Access Points (NAP): Connection points between different networks.

Network Architecture: The philosophy and organizational concept for enabling communications between equipment at multiple locations; detailed specifications outlining the processors, terminals and transmission media, protocols and software to be used to accomplish accurate communications.

Network Control Point (NCP): In virtual private networks, the Network Contol Point is a centralized database that stores a subscriber's unique VPN definition. Highly sophisticated, this database screens every call and applies call processing control in accordance with customer-defined requirements.

Network Element: As defined in the Telecommunications Act of 1996, a facility or equipment used in provisioning a telecommunications service. The term may include the features, functions and capabilities of that facility or equipment.

Network Interface Card: Also known as NIC. Add-in circuit board that allows a PC to be connected to a local area network (LAN).

Network Layer: The logical network entity that services the transport layer in the OSI model. It is responsible for ensuring that data passed to it from the transport layer is routed and delivered through the network.

Network License: A license from a software vendor that allows an application to be shared by many users over a network.

Network Operating System (NOS): NOS is software that controls the execution of network programmes and modules. Structurally, networking software comprises multiple modules, most residing in network servers, but some must be installed in each terminal/station that can access network resources. Peer-to-peer NOSs permit any terminal/station to act as a resource server or a client, and can be based on

Microsoft's Disk operating system (MS DOS) designed for IBM and compatible PCs. Since MS DOS is not designed to run multiple programmes and respond to many simultaneous users, most NOSs designed for large networks with dedicated servers/superservers, have a multitasking and multi- user architecture. Advanced NOS products support network management, diagnostics, and administration, as well as, primary server, client, de vice and external network driver functions.

Network Operators: The folks who install and maintain GSM cellular networks.

Network Portability Access Service (NPAS): A service which will make available to other network portability service providers (other telecommunications carriers) the central office equipment and facilities necessary for access to the public switched telephone network, enabling them to offer services similar to PrimeLine.

Network ring-again: A feature on a PBX that allows a caller, after encountering a busy signal, to be notified when the called line becomes free, provides the option of automatically reinstating the call.

Network Services: Network Services are specified sets of information transfer capabilities furnished to users between telecommunications network points of termination. Network services categories include access and transport, public and private, and switched and non-switched.

Network Topology: **(1)** Describes the physical and logical relationship of nodes in a network. **(2)** The schematic arrangement of the links and nodes of a network, typically either a star, ring, tree or bus topology, or some hybrid combination thereof.

Network Trunks: Circuits connecting switching centers.

Network user Identifier (NUI): On a packet network, the identification code used by a customer on a public dial port to identify him/herself to the network for billing purposes.

Network Virtual Terminal: A communications concept wherein a variety of DTEs, with different data rates, protocols, codes, and formats, are accommodated in the same network. This is done as a result of network processing, where each device's data is converted into a network standard format, then converted into the format of the receiving device at the destination end.

Network: **1.** Two or more information sources or destinations (points or nodes) linked via communications media to exchange information. **2.** It can be as simple as a cable strung between two computers a few feet apart or as complex as hundreds of thousands of computers around the world linked through fiber optic cables, phone lines and satellites.

Network Information Center (NIC): An organization which provides network users with information about services provided by the network. As close as an Internet- style network gets to a hub; it's usually where you'll find information about that particular network.

Network Numbering Exchange (NNX): Former three-digit location code which represented a central office. Now in NXX form, the available number of CO codes has been increased by permitting 0 and 1 as second digits in some circumstances.

Newbie: Someone who is new to the Internet. Sometimes used derogatorily by Net.veterans who have forgotten that, they, too, were once newbies who did not innately know the answer to everything. "Clueless newbie" is always derogatory.

Newly Competitive Service: A service that is characterized by open entry into the market and one that is subject to increasing competition but not yet viewed as fully competitive.

Newsreader: A programme to read news and providing capabilities for following or deleting threads.

NFS - Network File System: A network service that lets a programme running on one computer use data stored on a different computer on the same Internet as if it were on its own disk.

Nibble: Popular name for four bits, or half a byte.

No Ani: This condition means the PSAP received a call but no telephone number displayed on the workstation monitor.

The PSAP should report this condition immediately to Repair Service.

No Displays: The PSAP ALI display portion of the workstation monitor is blank. Try the Repeat ALI button for another look-up at the database. If screen is still blank, report this type of trouble immediately to Repair Service. If all monitors at the PSAP are blank, it is an indication that the problem is in the circuits from the PSAP to the E9-1-1 network computer.

Node: **(1)** In network topology, a terminal of any branch of a network or a terminal common to two or more branches of a network. **(2)** In a switched network, the switching points, including patch and control facilities. **(3)** In a data network, the location of a data station which interconnects data transmission lines. **(4)** A point in a standing wave at which the amplitude is at a minimum.

Noise Temperature: The amount of thermal noise present in a system, expressed in degrees Kelvin. The lower the noise temperature, the better.

Noise: **(1)** Unplanned energy introduced onto a communications path, resulting in transmission errors. Undesirable signals bearing no desired information. **(2)** The unpredictable difference between the observed data and the true process.

Non-blocking: A switching network having a sufficient number of paths such that an originating call can always reach any other idle station without encountering a busy signal.

Non-Composite Video Signal: A signal which contains only the picture signal and the blanking pulses.

Non-Duplication Rules: Restrictions placed on cable television systems which prohibit them from importing distant programming that is simultaneously available locally.

Non-Transparent Cellular Data: Non Transparent phones use a special error correction technique called RLP. Transparent phones data not incorprate the RLP error corerction techniqure and their data MIGHT be corrupted.

Nonvolatile Storage: A medium that maintains or keeps its contents when the power is removed.

Numbering Plan Area (NPA): A geographical boundary within which no two telephones will have the same seven-digit number. "N" is any number between two and nine, "P" is always one or zero; and "A" is any number excluding zero.

Number Portability: Number portability is the term used to describe capability of individuals, businesses, and organizations to retain their existing telephone number(s) -- and the same quality of service-when switching to a new local service provider.

O

Object Programme: **(1)** Fully compiled or assembled software that is ready to be loaded into the computer. (2) The output from processing a source programme through an assembler or compiler.

Off Hook: The signal that the telephone receiver has been lifted (activated). Originating off hook activates a dial tone on switched networks. Destination off hook completes a call (and activates minute-by-minute billing for long distance calls).

Office of Communications (OFCOM): The independent regulator and competition authority for the UK communications industries.

Off-line: **(1)** Condition that exists when devices or subsystems are not connected into, do not form a part of and/or are not subject to the same controls as an operational system. **(2)** A device which is not permanently connected to the processor or to external circuits.

Off-network Access Line (ONAL): **(1)** A connection from a private switched network to the public switched network. **(2)** The connection provided by a carrier and used in common by subscribers to enter and/or exit from the switched network.

Off-network Access Trunk (ONAT): The circuit between the CLEC switch and the trunk side of a telco office for FGB and FGD services.

Off-network Calling: Telephone calls which originate in or pass through private switching systems in transmission networks and are extended to stations in the public telephone system.

Off-premises Extension (OPX): Peripheral PBX equipment located in a building other than the one housing the PBX itself.

Off-Premises System: Refers to a teleconferencing room or equipment located outside of a user organization's facility; e.g., a video teleconferencing room operated by a vendor and available to the public for a fee.

Ohms Restriction: Ohms Restriction is the same as Ohms resistance. Ohms are measures of resistance. A resistance of one Ohm allows one Ampere of current to pass at the electric potential of one Volt.

On Hook: **(1)** Condition existing when the receiver or handset is resting on the switchhook. **(2)** The idle state (open loop) of a single telephone or PBX line loop.

On Network Calling: A call that originates and terminates on a private network.

On-Demand Bandwidth: Dialable digital bandwidth access using the public switched telephone network instead of dedicated facilities.

One Button Transfer: The ability to transfer a 9-1-1 call to another public safety agency by pressing one button; can be fixed or selective transfer.

One Plus - 1+: Customer ability to access the long distance service provider of their choice by first dialing 1, then the long distance number. Equal Access guaranteed by the 1982 AT&T MFJ. 1+ is an outbound service where the calling station pays the charges.

On-line System: A network interface which provides direct interface between applications programmes stored in the computer and terminals used for data entry and output.

On-line: When a computer is connected to an on-line service, bulletin-board system or public-access site, it is on-line.

Open Architecture: The manner in which the information highway is designed so that equipment of different manufacturers may be used, and content producers/providers are able to share information and any subsequent revenue opportunities.

Open Inter-network Accessibility: Refers to the capability of users of one network being able to readily access users of another network.

Open Network Architecture: Structure of a communications network that allows access by all types of terminals and users to any network capability without compatibility problems.

Open Outcry Auction: An auction in which bidders openly shout out their bids.

Open Systems Interconnection (OSI) Standards: OSI standards are standards for the exchange of information among systems that are "open" to one another by virtue of incorporating ISO standards. The OSI reference model segments communications functions into seven layers. Each layer relies on the next lower layer to provide more primitive functions and, in turn, provides services to support the next higher layer.

Open Video Systems (OVS): An Open Video System is similar to a cable system. In an OVS, the system operator must lease channel capacity to unaffiliated programmers at just, reasonable, and nondiscriminatory rates.

Operating System: A computer programme that runs the computer and handles data traffic between the disks and memory.

Operating Telephone Company: An operating telephone company is any Bell-operating company or independent telephone company (termed exchange carrier in the MFJ) operating in North America.

Operating Time: The time required for dialing a call, waiting for the connection to be established, coordinating the transmission with the personnel or equipment at the receiving end, and disconnecting after the transmission.

Operator Assisted Calls: (1) Direct distance dialing (DDD) calls which require and receive help by telephone company operators. (2) Person-to-person, collect calls, calling card calls from rotary phones, etc.

Operator Service Call - OSC: A call that is placed through a human or automated operator (0+).

Operator Service Provider (OSP): A common carrier that provides services from public phones, including payphones and hotel/motel phones.

Optical Amplifier: A device to amplify an optical signal without converting the signal from optical to electrical and back again to optical energy. The two most common optical amplifiers are erbium-doped fiber amplifiers (EDFAs), which amplify with a laser pump diode and a section of erbium-doped fiber, and semiconductor laser amplifiers.

Optical Character Recognition - OCR: The machine identification of printed characters through use of light-sensitive devices; often used as a method of entering data.

Optical Fiber: Any filament or fiber made of dielectric materials that is used to transmit light and/or to guide signals. [Optical fiber typically consists of a core, that carries the signal and cladding, a substance with a slightly higher refractive index than the core, which surrounds the core and serves to reflect the light signal back into it.]

Optical Receiver: Device that converts optical signals transmitted on a fiber optic line back into a replica of the original electrical signals.

Optical Transmitter: Source device that converts electrical signals into corresponding optical signals for transmission through fiber optic line. The source of the optical signal can be a light-emitting diode or solid-state laser.

Orange Book: Colloquial name of the standard that describes CD-Recordable equipment, media and formats. An extension of the "Yellow Book" standard which includes specifications for incremental writes or multiple sessions. It specifies standards for CD-R and magneto-optical cartridge systems as well as Kodak's Photo CD. Most CD-ROM drives today can only read "single session" discs or the first session of a multisession disc.

Orderwire: A channel used by installers to expedite the provisioning of lines.

Original Equipment Manufacturer (OEM): (1) Producer of a product made for assembly into a final system or larger subassembly by another.

Originating Communications Provider (OCP): Also known as Originating Networks', the OCP is a phone network (e.g. BT) that sends you your phone bill and connects your call from your phone through to its destination (the number you have dialled).

Originating Office: The central office that serves the calling party.

Origination Site: The location from which video and/or audio is transmitted and uplinked in a teleconference. Other sites participating are receive sites.

OS (Operations System): Sophisticated applications software that overlooks the entire network.

OSI Seven-layer Model: A standard architecture for data communications. Layers define hardware and software required for multi-vendor information processing equipment to be mutually compatible. The seven layers from lowest to highest are: physical, link, network, transport, session, presentation, and application.

OSS: Operations support systems or operational support system other common carriers (OCC): Specialized common carriers, domestic or international record carriers and domestic satellite carriers engaged in providing private line services (voice, data, audio or video) as authorized by the FCC.

Out Of Band Signaling: Out of band signaling uses the same channel path as the voice traffic but signaling is in a frequency band outside that used for the voice traffic. In digital systems, out-of-band signaling may take the appearance of an allocated bit position or a dedicated channel or time slot.

Outage Time: Accumulated interval between unavailable and restoration time. It begins when a customer releases the circuit for repair and ends when the circuit is returned to the customer.

Outage: (1) Any disruption of service. (2) The point at which a customer releases a circuit for repair, lasting until the circuit is returned to the customer in working condition.

Outbound Telemarketing: Any outgoing call designed to sell or service a customer or prospect.

Outbound: Direction of a signal relative to the hub of a local area network (LAN) or other telecommunications system. Outbound signals would be traveling away from the primary hub in the forward direction to the extremities of the system.

Outgoing Calls: The switching functions are usually performed in a central office. Digital Centrex offers the advanced features of fourth generation PBXs, without the need to purchase or lease equipment and, in most cases, eliminates the need for floor space, electrical prime power and heating, ventilation and air conditioning.

Out-of-band Signaling: Use of a separate data link which is not in the voice circuit to transmit call set-up and ANI information from carrier to carrier, or from carrier to customer.

Out-of-band: (1) Any entity outside an assigned range, scope or magnitude. (2) Any frequency outside the spectrum used for voice.

Overbuild: Adding radio capacity to a telecommunications network.

Overflow: (1) Switching equipment which operates when the traffic load exceeds the capacity of the regular equipment. (2) Traffic which is handled on overflow equipment. (3) Traffic which exceeds switching capacity and is lost. (4) The carry digit in a digital computer. (5) Intermediate message storage which serves as an extension of in-transit storage to preclude system saturation; an example, magnetic tape.

Overhead: Extra bits in a digital stream used to carry information besides traffic signals. Orderwire, for example, would be considered overhead information.

Overlay Area Code: New area code in a region issued in addition to the existing area code.

P

P Factor: Grade of service which describes the percentage of blocked calls. For example, P.10 means that 10 percent of all calls were blocked; P.01 means that 1 percent of all calls were blocked.

PABX - Private Automatic Branch Exchange: A private automatic telephone exchange, usually located at the user's site, that routes and interfaces the local business telephones and data circuits to and from the public telephone network.

Packet Assembler/Disassembler (PAD): **(1)** A non-adjustable resistance network used to insert transmission loss into a circuit. **(2)** To fill a block with dummy data, usually zeros or blanks.

Packet Loss: Loss of parts of the packetized data that comprises the whole communication.

Packet Switching: A communications data transmission method that breaks down messages into smaller units of standard sized pieces called packets, which are individually addressed and routed through a network; the network link is occupied only during packet transmission. Packet switching increases efficiency in transport.

Packet: Collection of bits comprising data and control information formatted for transmission from one node to another. One of the key features of a packet is that it contains the destination address in addition to the data. Each packet can contain up to 512 bytes, or about 100 words.

Packetization: Breaking down of data that a computer sends into smaller pieces (known as packets). Each packet has a header that identifies the packet and its destination. The packet travels through routers to its destination computer, which reassembles all the packets that belong together and then sends this reconstituted data to the appropriate programme.

PAD Character: A fill character inserted when insufficient data characters are present to satisfy a field length requirement.

Paging System: A one-way mobile radio service where a user carries a small, lightweight miniature radio receiver capable of responding to coded signals. These devices, called "pagers," emit an audible signal, vibrate or do both when activated by an incoming message.

PAL: Phase Alternation by Line, the 625-line, 25-frame-per-second TV standard used in Western Europe, India, China, Australia, New Zealand, Argentina, and parts of Africa. Brazil uses PAL-M, a 525-line variant.

PANS: Curiously enough, this stands for Pretty Amazing New Services/Stuff and is often used to describe ISDN capabilities.

Parabolic Dish: A satellite antenna, usually bowl-shaped, that concentrates signals to a single focal point.

Parallel Input/Output: Inputting data to or outputting data from, storage in whole information elements, e.g., a word rather than a bit at a time. Typically, each bit of a word has its own wire for data transmission, so that all of the bits of a word can be transmitted simultaneously.

Parallel Port: An output port on a PC that transmits data eight bits (one byte) at a time.

Parity Bit: Most modems have the capability to send an extra bit for every byte sent, which is used to help sense errors. This is called the parity bit. It can be set to no parity, mark parity, space parity, odd parity or even parity. Most BBS's do not use a parity bit.

Parity Check: A check of the accuracy of data being transmitted. To accomplish this, an extra parity bit is added to a group of bits so that the number of ones in the group is, according to the specification, even or odd. Then, at the receiving end, the bits in the word are added, the parity bit needed for that total is determined.

Parity Checking: One of the oldest error checking techniques. Character bit patterns are forced into parity (total number of bits odd or even) by adding a 1 or 0 bit as appropriate, as they are transmitted. The parity (odd or even) is then verified upon receipt by the receiving device.

Partial Displays: The PSAP receives an ANI display, but the display is incomplete (missing alpha or numeric characters). Try the Repeat ALI button for another lookup at the database. If the screen is still garbled, report this to Repair Service.

Partially Dedicated Access: Long distance carrier access method in which a non-local call is carried by the long distance carrier via a dedicated trunk facility for either the first or last part of the call's journey, and on the carrier's network for the middle part of the journey. Also called "dedicated to switched," "switched to dedicated," "on-net to off-net" and "off-net to on-net."

Patch: **(1)** To make an improvised modification **(2)** To change a software routine in a rough or expedient way. (3) A temporary electrical connection.

Path Overhead (POH): Overhead accessed, generated, and processed by path-terminating equipment. Path overhead includes nine bytes of STS Path Overhead and, when the frame is VT-structured, five bytes of VT Path Overhead.

Path Table: One of two tables contained in the volume descriptor of a CD-ROM, which comprise the file management system for the disc. The path table contains the names of all directories on the disc, and is the fastest way to access a directory that is not close to the root directory.

Path Terminating Equipment (PTE): Network elements, such as fiber-optic terminating systems, which can access, generate, and process Path Overhead.

Path: A logical connection between a point where an STS or VT is multiplexed to the point where it is demultiplexed.

Payload Pointer: Indicates the beginning of the Synchronous Payload Envelope.

Payload: The portion of the SONET signal available to carry service signals such as DS1 and DS3. The contents of an STS SPE or VT SPE.

Pay-per-society: The idea that the pay-per-view video concept will work for all areas of an information society. Many on-line services already charge by the minute or have monthly rates.

Pay-Per-View - PPV: Usage-based fee structure used sometimes in cable television programming in which the user is charged a price for individual programmes requested.

Payphone Charge: The charge per unit to make a phone call. Also used as the additional charge per call for a calling card or dialaround system if call is made using a payphone, normally collected for the owner of the payphone.

Payphone Fee: Additional charge per call if if call is made using a payphone, normally collected for the owner of the payphone.

Payphone Surcharge: Additional charge per call if if call is made using a payphone, normally collected for the owner of the payphone.

Payphone: A public (or private) telephone that accepts coins or encoded credit cards.

PBX: A PBX (private branch exchange) is a telephone system within an enterprise that switches calls between enterprise users on local lines while allowing all users to share a certain number of external phone lines. The main purpose of a PBX is to save the cost of requiring a line for each user to the telephone company's central office. The PBX is owned and operated by the enterprise rather than the telephone company (which may be a supplier or service provider, however). Private branch exchanges used analog technology originally. Today, PBXs use digital technology (digital signals are converted to analog for outside calls on the local loop using plain old telephone service).

PC Cards: Previously known as PCMCIA cards, these are credit card devices used in notebooks and desktop readers for inter alia, data/fax, storage, GPS puposes.

PCM (Pulse Code Modulation): Sampling technique for digitizing analog signals, especially audio signals. PCM samples the signal 8,000 times a second. PCM is used with T-1 and T-3 carrier systems. These carrier systems combine the PCM signals from many lines and transmit them over a single cable or other medium.

PCMCIA: A credit card sized card that generally plugs into a notebook computer. It conforms to the Personal Computer Memory Card International Association spec. Now known as PC Cards.

PCS Encompasses: cordless phones, cellular mobile phone, paging systems, personal communications networks, wireless office phone systems and any other wireless telecommunications systems that allow people to place and receive voice/data calls while away from home and office.

PDA (Personal Digital Assistant): Small computing device that uses wireless technology to transmit and receive data. The handheld PDA's software usually includes a name and address database, to-do list and note taker. PDA users use either a stylus to make selections on on-screen menus or enter printed characters on a small on-screen keypad.

PDIAL List: List of public providers that offer full Internet access.

Percent Denial: (1) A measure of the grade of service provided on a dial access circuit group; the average percentage of attempts blocked or denied due to a busy condition during the busy hour.

Peripheral: Device such as a communications terminal that is external to the system processor.

Personal Communications: Personal communications provides at least one human operator with direct terminal access and real time or near real time interactive communications with a remote human opera tor or an information system resource. Personal communications can refer to a broad range of services, systems and equipment, e.g., facsimile machines, landline telephones, cellular tele phone systems and emerging personal communication system (PCS) adjuncts, and a variety of radio systems including pagers, hand-held remote data entry terminals, and autonomous citizen-band-like radio systems.

Personal Communications Service (pcs): Any of several types of wireless, voice and/or data communications systems, typically incorporating digital technology. PCS licenses are most often used to provide services similar to advanced cellular mobile or paging services. However, PCS can also be used to provide other wireless communications services, including services that allow people to place and receive communications while away from their home or office, as well as wireless communications to homes, office buildings and other fixed locations.

Personal Identification Number (PIN): Personal unique security codes that callers use to access their accounts.

Personalized Response System (PRS): A computer assistance system which permits operators to pre-record their greeting to customers and other frequently used messages, thereby relieving stress on their voices and increasing operator productivity.

Person-to-person call: A type of long distance call. Charging begins only when the person calling begins speaking to the person to whom they have specified they wish to speak.

Person-to-Person: Operator assisted phone call - only billed if the specified person is available.

Petition For Reconsideration:A Petition for Reconsideration is a written request submitted to the FCC for review of an action it has previously taken. Applicants have 30 days after a Report and Order is published in the Federal Register to file comments with the FCC. The agency will consider public comments, replies, and industry concerns before finalizing its initial decision. As a result of the review process, the FCC will either issue a Memorandum Opinion and Order amending its initial decision, or deny the Petition for Reconsideration.

Phase: A fraction, expressed in degrees, of one complete cycle of a wave form or orbit. Photonics: Gallium arsenide integrated circuits for optical interconnections within and between computer and communication equipment called GaA. Present fiber optic computer and communication links are limited by discrete component electronics. In development is a projected 32-channel parallel monolithic IC connector which could vastly increase performance and drive down costs to open up long- sought new fiber optic markets which can replace current copper-wired connections.

Phase Jitter: A random distortion of signal lengths. [Phase jitter interferes with interpretation of information by changing the timing.

Phase Modulation (PM): A modulation technique in which the phase of a signal is altered to differentiate between a binary 1 and 0.

Phosphor: Material which coats the back side of a CRT screen.

Photon: The basic unit of light transmission used to define the lowest (physical) layer in the OSI seven-layer model.

Phreaker: Aperson who spends a lot of time trying to find out as much as possible about the telephone company [like South Africa's TELKOM], and how it works. They often try to find out ways to make long distance calls for free. Some steal calls from telephone credit card users, some steal calls from the phone company directly, and others don't make "free" long distance calls. They are sometimes confused with hackers.

Physical Layer: Within the OSI model, lowest level of network processing below the link layer that is concerned with the electrical, mechanical and handshaking procedures over the interface that connects a device to a transmission medium (example, RS-232-C).

PIC Charge: The one-time fee charged by the LEC to the customer to change the PIC on an ANI from one long distance company's 10xxx access code to another.

PIC Freeze: A PIC Freeze prevents the long distance from being switched for the specified ANIs. Useful to prevent slamming, or the unauthorized switching of long distance services.

PIC Request: A request record sent to a LEC asking for an ANI to be activated, deactivated or changed in some way.

PIC Response: A response record sent by a LEC (corresponding to a previous PIC Request) with response code that indicates whether the request was performed.

Picture Element (pixel): **(1)** A single dot on a computer display. **(2)** The smallest discrete part of a video image, the size of which is controlled by an analog-to-digital conversion sampling process.

Picture Element: One of many monochrome or color "dots" that comprise a television picture (also called pixel or pel).

Picture Signal: That portion of the composite video signal which lies above the blanking level and contains the picture brightness information.

Picture Tube: The television cathode-ray tube used to reproduce and display an image created by variations of intensity of the electron beam which scans the coated surface on the tube interior.

Pilot Telephone Number: The entire seven-digit telephone number will be displayed on the ALI screen. The pilot telephone number is the main number of the telephone service. This information would be important if someone dials 9-1-1 from an outward-only line and then hangs up. The PSAP would be unable to reach them at that number, but would be able to reach someone at the main number. In most cases, the pilot telephone number and the actual telephone number are the same.

Ping: A programme that can trace the route a message takes from your site to another site.

Pipe: Telecommunications transmission line or cable with significant bandwidth capacity.

Pixel: The smallest area of a television picture capable of being sampled, transmitted through a system and displayed on a monitor.

PKZIP: The programme which will create an archive with the extension "ZIP". It is one of the most popular archive programmes.

Platform: Refers to different computer types or operating environments; e.g., Macintosh, DOS/Windows, CD-I and Sega are different platforms.

Plesiochronous: A network with nodes timed by separate clock sources with almost the same timing.

PMS: Property Management System - A software programme and computer that controls all guest billing and guest services functions in a hotel. In short, the guts of a hotel's computer system. Some telephone systems have a PMS interface which allows various degrees of integration between the telephone system and the hotel's computer systems. For example, voicemail could be administered throught the Hotel's Property Management System.

Point Of Presence - POP: The physical access location interface between a local exchange carrier and an Interexchange

Carrier fiber network. The point to which the telephone company terminates a subscriber's circuit for long distance service or leased line communications.

Pointer: A part of the SONET overhead that locates a floating payload structure. STS pointers locate the SPE. VT Pointers locate floating mode virtual tributaries. All SONET frames use STS pointers; only floating mode virtual tributaries use VT pointers.

Point-to-Multipoint: A teleconference broadcast from one location to several receiving locations (also known as downlink sites.)

Point-to-point Circuit: A private communications link between two terminations which does not connect with a public telephone system.

Point-to-Point Protocol (PPP): Protocol to access the Internet using dial-up connections.

Polar Keying: Technique of current loop signaling in which electrical flow direction establishes the two-level binary code.

Polarization: A characteristic of the electric field on an electromagnetic wave in space.

Pole Attachment: A communications relay or receiving device attached to a pole, duct or conduit owned or controlled by a utility company.

Poll: An individual control message from a central controller to an individual station on a multipoint network inviting that station to send.

Polling: **1.** Network control in which the control station invites tributary stations to transmit in the sequence specified by the control station. **2.** In point-to-point or multipoint communication, the process whereby stations are invited one at a time to transmit. **3.** Sequential interrogation of devices for various purposes, such as avoiding contention, determining operational status, or determining readiness to send or receive data.

Polycarbonate: Material from which compact discs are made.

POP (Point-of-Presence): A point in the network where inter-exchange carrier facilities like DS3 or OC-N meet with access facilities managed by telephone companies or other service providers.

Port: In software, the act of converting code so that a programme runs on more than one type of computer. In networking, a number that identifies a specific "channel" used by network services. For instance, Gopher generally uses port 70 but is occasionally set to use other ports on various machines.

Portable Transmitter: A transmitter so constructed that it may be moved about conveniently from place to place but not ordinarily used while in motion, although some portable communications equipment does provide the capability to used while in motion.

Post: To compose a message for a Usenet newsgroup and then send it out for others to see.

Postal, Telephone and Telegraph (PTT): International administration, usually government controlled, which manages and operates postal and telecommunications services outside the country. Typically a monopoly operation.

Postmaster: The person to contact at a particular site to ask for information about the site or complain about one of his/her user's behavior.

Post-Production: For a programme which is not a live broadcast, all the footage would be shot with the talent on a set constructed for the purpose or in remote locations. After the shooting, the post-production begins. The tape is electronically edited on video editing equipment. Music and graphics might be added. When the editing is finished, the programme is complete. It then might be sold as a training video, situation comedy, drama, etc. Most commercial productions are produced this way, even though it might appear to be a live broadcast.

PostScript: A page-description language, developed by Adobe Systems, that converts any computer image - whether text or graphics - to a form that compatible output devices can interpret and print. PostScript typefaces can be printed on any PostScript compatible printer.

POTS (Plain Old Telephone Service): Telephone service that most homes use. The main distinctions between POTS and non-POTS services are speed and bandwidth, with POTS generally restricted to about 52 kbps. High-speed, digital communications lines such as ISDN are not POTS.

Power user: A computer user who is quite skilled in the use of computers over a variety of applications.

PPP - Point-to-Point Protocol: PPP provides a method for transmitting datagrams over serial point-to-point links. pps: Packets per second.

Premastering: The process of logically formatting an authored application and database. A working application or database converted to a standardized format such as ISO 9660 ready for writing to a final compact disc.

Premises Distribution System (PDS): PDS is the transmission network inside a building or among a group of buildings, for example an office park or a campus. PDS is used in this book as a generic term although AT&T used it to describe a specific product offering. The PDS connects desktop and other station equipment with common host equipment, (e.g., switches, computers and building automation systems), and to external telecommunications networks.

Premium Channels: Channels not included in a cable provider's regular service tiers. There are additional monthly fees charged for receiving premium channels.

Premium Rate: Premium rate services offer some form of information or entertainment that is charged to your phone bill. Premium rate calls are the most expensive and will cost between 10p and £1.50 from a BT landline (charges from other networks may vary). Premium rate numbers begin with 090 or 091 or use mobile shortcodes that are 4, 5 or 6 digits long.

Pre-Produced Segments: Video segments done prior to the day of the broadcast/production. These are videotaped and edited segments which will be shown during the broadcast to take the audience into the field for interviews, demonstrations, or on site visits to places that somehow embody the content. For example, in a programme about environmental pollution, a pre-produced segment might show a polluted stream with beer cans and dead fish. It might show the source of the pollution such as chemical or sewage processing plants.

Pre-Production: The first phase of a videoconference. Pre-production includes planning, research, script writing, developing taped segments to be dropped into a live production, hiring and rehearsing talent, and anything else done up to minute the broadcast begins.

Prescribed Interexchange Charge (picc): The charge the local exchange company assesses the long distance company when a consumer picks it as his or her long distance carrier.

Presentation Layer: The OSI processing layer that provides services to the application layer, allowing it to interpret the data exchanged as well as structure data messages to be transmitted in a specific display and control format.

Prestel: The British Post Offices public viewdata service. PRI - Primary rate interface: PRI is a CCITT-defined ISDN trunking technology that delivers 64 kbps clear channels and standardized out-of-band signaling. PRI can serve customer premise equipment (CPE) such as a PBX, LAN gateway, or host computer or can serve as a trunk interface between central offices.

Presubscription: This term is used to describe the selection of a particular long-distance carrier to handle all calls for "1+dialing" zones.

Presubscription: This term is used to describe the selection of a particular long distance carrier to handle all calls for "1+dialing" zones.

Preventive Maintenance: Precautionary measures taken on a system to forestall failures by providing for systematic inspection, detection and correction of incipient problems before they develop into major defects.

PRI: Primary Rate Interface. An ISDN term used internationally define an ISDN version T-1 trunk from the customer premises to the edge of the ISDN service provider network. Also knwo as a 23B+D, PRI supports 24 channels, in total. The 23 B (Bearer) channels are information-bearing channels; that is to say that each channel supports the transfer of actual user data. Each of these channels is a "clear channel". A clear channel runs at 64 Kbps. The D (Data or Delta) channel, which aslo runs at 64 Kbps, is used for all singaling and control purposes. The D channel also can be used for end user packet data transfer when not in use for its primary function of signaling and control.

Primary Interexchange Carrier (PIC): In an equal access environment, the term primary interexchange carrier (PIC) refers to the long distance provider designated by the customer as their preferred long distance provider.

Primary Path: The preferred route from one switched node to another.

Primary Routing Point: The switch designated as the control point for a long-haul telephone call.

Prime Focus: Type of feed in a parabolic dish antenna which is positioned above the dish as the antennas focal point.

Printed Circuit (PC) Board: A circuit board whose electrical connections are made through conductive material that is contained on the board itself, rather than with individual wires.

Printer Font: The software that contains the image of a typeface in outline form; used by a laser printer or imagesetter to produce the image on paper or film. Also called outline font.

Private Automatic Branch Exchange (PABX): Now frequently known simply as PBX. A privately operated switching system with exchange lines to a public telecommunications system (e.g. BT or Mercury Networks) and capable of having an operator console connected to it. The term was originally devised to differentiate the PABX from the PMBX. It is now being superseded by the term PBX.

Private automatic exchange (PAX): Small, local, automatic telephone office, normally serving extensions in a business complex, typically without external lines to the public network.

Private Branch Exchange (PBX): A PBX is a premises switching system, serving a commercial or government organization, and usually located on that organization's premises. PBXs provide telecommunications services on the premises or campus, (e.g., internal calling and other services), and access to public and private telecommunications network services.

Private Exchange Master List (PXML): Lists of all the permissible uses of and attachment to a PABX.

Private Home Viewing: The viewing of television in a private home with reception by satellite equipment that is operated by an individual in that household and which serves only that household. It is a secondary transmission (via satellite) of a primary transmission of a television station licensed by the FCC.

Private Line Service: Dedicated telecommunications channels provided between two points or switched among multiple points. Privately leased for high-volume voice, data, audio or video transmissions.

Private Line: Uses dedicated circuits to connect customer's equipment at both ends of the line. Does not provide any switching capability (unless supported by customer premise equipment). Usually includes two local loops and an IEC circuit.

Private Network: A private network is a network made up of circuits and, sometimes, switching equipment, for the exclusive use of one organization.

Private Radio Service: Radio communications authorized for local governments and private enterprises. Amateur and citizen band radio are private radio services as are several other services in the categories of: Aviation, Marine, Public Safety, Industrial, Land Transportation and Microwave.

Private use Network: Two or more channels contracted for by a customer and restricted for use by that customer only.

Product Overview: A brief definition of a product and/or service used in written methods and procedures.

Programme: A series of instructions or statements assembled in a form acceptable to a computer and prepared to achieve a certain result.

Programme Day/Date/Local Time: Broadcast times are usually listed in Eastern Standard Time or Eastern Daylight Time depending upon the time of the year. Remember to convert this to the local time.

Programme Log: Records once kept by a broadcasting station in a public file which provided a record of programmes broadcast, programme type and programme length. The logs also included commercial and public service spots. Broadcasters are no longer required to maintain programme logs.

Programming Language: An artificial language, established for expressing computer programmes, which uses a set of characters and rules whose meanings are assigned prior to use.

Projection Television: A combination of lenses and/or mirrors that project an enlarged television picture on a screen.

PROM - Programmable read-only memory: A type of read-only memory that can be programmed by the computer user. This programming usually requires special equipment.

Prompt: 1. Any symbol or message presented to an operator by an operating system, indicating a condition of readiness, location, or that particular information is needed before a programme can proceed. **2.** When the host system asks you to do something and waits for you to respond.

Proprietary: A device or programme designed and owned by a particular manufacturer or vendor, as opposed to a standard. CD-ROM drives are manufactured to read discs that comply with the Yellow Book standard, but their controller cards may be either supplied by the manufacturer (proprietary) or based on the Small Computer Systems Interface (standard).

PRO-Que Channel: PRO is a term used primarily in television transmissions to designate a separate audio voice grade signal sent with a television channel which is used for programme instructions and queuing for the broadcast engineers. The voice quality 3 kHz channel may contain audio or data as may most be appropriate for the specific application. It is not received by a standard television receiver without special equipment.

Prospect Profile: A detailed description of a potential customer; the profile generally includes financial, demographic, industry, job title and past buying history information.

Protocol Conversion: Process of translating communications formats and timing, which would otherwise be incompatible, into messages understood by the network. Performed by a dedicated device, a software package loaded onto an existing system or by a value-added (intelligent) network.

Protocol: A set of rules and procedures for establishing and controlling conversations on a line. The set of messages has specific formats for exchanging communications and assuring end-to-end data integrity of links, circuits, messages, sessions and application processes. Usually associated with communications over computer. It is the language that computers use when talking to each other. The method used to transfer a file between a host system and your computer. A formal description of message formats and the rules two computers must follow to exchange those messages. There are several types, such as Kermit, YMODEM and ZMODEM. Protocols can describe lowlevel details of machine-to-machine interfaces (e.g., the order in which bits and bytes are sent across a wire) or high-level exchanges between allocation programmes (e.g., the way in which two programmes transfer a file across the Internet).

Provisioning: The process by which a requested (ordered) service is designed, implemented and tracked (providing the subcomponent parts).

PSAP Public Safety Answering Point: A facility operated on a twenty-four hour basis, assigned the responsibility of receiving 9-1-1 calls and, as appropriate, directly dispatching emergency response services, or transferring or relaying 9-1-1 calls to other public safety agencies. The PSAP is the first point of reception of a 9-1-1 call.

PSK: Phase Shift Keying. In this method of modulation/demodulation, there are two frequencies used (usually 1200 hertz and 2400 hertz). There are 4 different phase angles (0, 90, 180, and 270 degrees), representing dibits 00, 01, 10, and 11. This is usually used for 1200bps transmission: Note that the baud rate using PSK is really ½ of the bps rate, since 2 bits are sent at a time instead of one.

PSTN (Public Switched Telephone Network): Combined transmission facilities of the world's telephone networks, including those available to subscribers on an unrestricted basis. In the United States, the PSTN is regulated by the FCC.

Public Access Channel: A cable television channel specifically designated as a noncommercial public access channel available on a first-come, non-discriminatory basis.

Public Access Provider: An organization that provides Internet access for individuals or other organizations, often for a fee.

Public Data Network: A network established and operated by a telecommunications administration or a recognized private operating agency for the specific purpose of providing data transmission services to the public.

Public Dial Port: A dial-in port which provides access to a system or service, such as a packet network, from a terminal connected to the public telephone network.

Public Notice (PN): A Public Notice is issued by the Commission to notify the public of an action taken or an upcoming event.

Public Switched Network (PSN): Any switching system that provides a circuit switched to many customers.

Public Switched Telephone Network (PSTN): The worldwide dial-up telephone network or a portion of that network (e.g., the Bell Canada PSTN). A phrase often used when referring to data or other non-telephone services carried over a path initially established using normal telephone signaling and ordinary switched long distance telephone circuits.

PUC - Public Utilities Commission: The agency regulating intrastate phone service.

Pulse Code Modulation (PCM): A modulation technique in which the signal being transmitted is sampled at regular intervals to determine its magnitude. The magnitude is converted to a digital pulse for transmission.

Pulse Dialing: A method that some phones use to dial numbers. It involves a series of "clicks." Most modems support this type of dialing, which is the only type available in some remote areas. The other method of dialing is tone dialing.

Pulse Modulation: The modulation of the characteristics of a series of pulses in one of several ways to represent the information-bearing signal. The most common pulse modulation in telephony is pulse code modulation.

Pulse: **(1)** A signal that can be wholly described by a constant amplitude and the duration time. **(2)** Signal form typically used internally in computers, terminals and other business machines as well as in communications facilities.

Pushbutton Dialing: Type of signaling which emits two distinct frequencies for each indicated digit.

Q

Quality Improvement Process (QIP): A team-based, structured, problem-solving process aimed at achieving exceptional customer satisfaction.

Quantizing Noise: In any analog to digital conversion process, e.g., PCM, quantizing noise is the difference between the converted binary value and the actual analog signal's amplitude.

Quarter Common Intermediate Format (QCIF): A subset of the coded video signals transmitted when using CCITT Rec. H.261 coding methods.

Queue: **(1)** To arrange or form in a line. **(2)** A waiting line. **(3)** A series of elements, one waiting behind the other. **(4)** A temporary delay in providing service caused by the inability of the particular system to handle the number of messages or calls attempted (example, a call queued for the least expensive route).

Queued Telecommunications Access Method (QTAM): Method used to transfer data between main storage and remote terminals; may also be employed for data collection, message switching and many other teleprocessing efforts involving queued messages or direct access storage devices.

QuickTime: Apple's multimedia extension to its System 7 operating software for the Macintosh. It is a time-based management system for combining text, graphics, sound, still images, animations and video. The software incorporates its own compression technology so that digitized movies can be stored and played off of a computer hard disk.

Quorum: At the FCC, the minimum number of Commissioners required to be present at a meeting or to participate in voting by circulation before the Commission can validly proceed to transact business. A quorum consists of a majority of the Commissioners.

R

Radar: A radio determination system based on the comparison of reference signals with radio signals reflected, or retransmitted, from the position to be determined.

Radiation: The outward flow of energy from any source in the form of radio waves.

Radio Common Carrier (RCC): A communications carrier that provides radio paging and mobile telephone services to the public.

Radio Frequency ((RF) : Radio frequencies are generally considered as any electromagnetic signal from normal radio to microwave transmission.

Radio Determination: The determination of the position, velocity and/or other characteristics of an object, or the obtaining of information relating to these parameters by means of the propagation properties of radio waves.

Radiotelephony: The use of radio to communicate sounds (e.g., speech).

Rain Attenuation - Rain Losses: The attenuation (loss) of a signal due to rainfall. If you are receiving a teleconference on a Ku band dish, local rainstorms can drastically weaken the signal strength of the programme. The result will be sparkles which interfere with the ability to see the programme. During a heavy downpour or thunderstorm, signal reception may be lost temporarily. The noise temperature perceived by the receiving antenna may increase due to rain being present in the link.

Random Access Memory (RAM) : The primary memory in a computer. The "random access" part of its name comes from the fact that the next "bit" of information in RAM can be located - no matter where it is - in an equal amount of time. This means that access to and from RAM memory is extraordinarily fast. By contraast, other storage media (magnetic tape) store information serially, one bit after another. Therefore you have to search for them and your search time will depend on how from from the bit you're searching for you are. Floppy disks are faster than magnetic tape because their information is readily at hand, though the read/write head will have to search for it. Hard disks are even faster because there are multiple heads and because the disks spin faster and everything moves faster. RAM memory is the fastest of all.

Raster: Scanning pattern used in generating, recording or reproducing television, facsimile or graphics images on a screen.

Rate Center: Specific geographic location used by LECs to determine interchange mileage for rate determination purposes.

Rate Element: A recurring fixed charge for IEC or LEC service at the lowest level. A local loop may have multiple rate elements associated with it, which make up the fixed portion of the monthly bill. For example: Local Access, Local Mileage, Entrance facilities, Channel Termination, Interexchange, etc.

Rate Group: A classification used by telephone companies to determine a customer's flat rate for local service. A customer's rate group is based on the number of telephone numbers a customer can call from their exchange without paying long distance charges.

Rate Mileage: Airline distance from one subscriber's rate center to all other LEC rate centers.

Rate of Return on Average Common Equity: The net earnings of a company applicable to common shareholders (before extraordinary items) divided by the company's average total common equity, multiplied by 100.

Rate Periods: Division of a day into categories for charges: day, evening, night/weekend.

Rate Rebalancing: The process by which the rates for long distance services are reduced while the rates for local services are increased to bring the rates for each more in line with the costs of providing them.

Rate Table: A database containing cost of a call based on area code and time of day.

Rates and Tariffs: Standards published by AT&T, OCCs,LECs, and IECs that define service availability, cost and provisioning procedures.

Rational Pricing: Pricing in which contribution levels have been reduced to market-sustainable levels, while the rate levels for individual services within the utility (i.e., local service) segment have been set at levels that are more closely reflective of the costs of providing such services.

RBOC (Regional Bell Operating Company): One of the seven local telephone companies created by the breakup of the AT&T system in 1984. RBOCs include Ameritech, Bell Atlantic, Bell South, NYNEX, Pacific Telesis Group, Southwestern Bell and U.S. West. Some of these entities have merged or been acquired by other companies and no longer exist as RBOCs.

Reach: "Reach" refers to the availability of a service in the community. It is the number of homes to which the service is available regardless of whether or not residents choose to subscribe.

Read Only Memory (ROM): Portion of computer memory which is programmed electrically by the manufacturer, is unchangeable and is unaffected by a power loss.

Real Time: **1.** The actual time during which a physical process occurs. **2.** Pertaining to the performance of a computation during the actual time that the related physical process occurs, in order that results of the computation can be used in guiding the physical process.

Real-Time Transport Protocol (RTP): Protocol that improves Internet telephone calls by adding special information to the voice data packets to help programmes reassemble them more efficiently.

Rebiller: An entity that resells another long distance company's service. Unlike an agent, the rebiller retains rights to the customer as the rebiller is the actual customer so far as the long distance company is concerned since the rebiller provides their own customer service to the customer and renders to the customer their own bill.

Receive Site: The site receiving the transmission from the origination site. A video teleconference might have 100 or more receive sites.

Receiver - Satellite: Electronic unit capable of receiving video and audio signals from satellites, usually from only one satellite at a time.

Receivers: Convert satellite signals into channels viewed (one at a time) on a TV monitor; designed to tune-in the format, bandwidth, and audio sub-carrier. Programmes broadcast in code (encryption) are decoded at receive sites. Basic Receivers: Lowest cost; limited (or manual) channel tuning capability; may use fixed antennas. Multi-Format Receivers: Most versatile; adjusts for all broadcast formats; receive any satellite video programme in six or more bandwidth selections, and two agile audio subcarrier switches; usually a motorized systems.

Recharge Code: A set of numbers on a calling card used to add additional funds, usually the last several digits of a PIN.

Rechargeable Phone Card: A calling card used which can be refilled with units by the addition of funds to the calling card account without the purchase of a new card or a new PIN.

Recorded Announcement Device (RAD): A device which automatically answers a line and delivers a pre-recorded message. Often used to tell a caller that they are in a queue and will be dealt with as soon as possible.

Recordnot Found: If the host computer is unable to do a look-up on a given ANI request from the PSAP, it will forward a Record Not Found message to the PSAP ALI screen. This could be the result of service order activity for a given individual not being processed into the E9-1-1 database, or problems with the host computer system whereby the records cannot be accessed.

Red Video Signal: A video transmission in which the red (R) green (G) and blue (B) picture components are present as individual signals.

Redundancy: **(1)** Duplicate standby equipment or facilities that are activated to insure continuous service or minimize the effect of equipment malfunctions.

Redundancy: Part of a message that can safely be omitted/deleted without ruining the integrity of a message; backup systems in case of main system failure.

Redundant Power: Secondary, separate electric power source in addition to the primary utility source. It may be a standby generator or a second electrical line, meter, and panel box from the electric utility.

Reflector: Antenna's main curved "dish," which collects and focus signals onto the secondary reflector or the feed.

Regeneration: Process of receiving distorted signal pulses and from them recreating new pulses at the correct repetition rate, pulse amplitude and pulse width.

Regenerator: Device that restores a degraded digital signal for continued transmission; also called a repeater.

Regional Bell Operating Companies (RBOCs): Seven independent regional holding companies which were formed, coincident with the divestiture of AT&T in 1984, to take over ownership of the Bell operating companies within their region. These companies are: Nynex; Bell Atlantic; BellSouth; Southwestern Bell; US West; Pacific Telesis and Ameritech. The RBOCs have set up numerous unregulated subsidiaries which are engaged in a variety of communications-related and non-communications businesses.

Regional Dynamic Routing: Dynamically controlled routing within a geographic region.

Regulated Rate of Return: Bell Canada's utility services are subject to rate of return regulation (i.e., return on average total capital), which is determined by the CRTC for regulatory purposes. After taking into account the costs of debt and preferred equity capital, this represents the regulated rate of return on average common equity. The regulated rate of return on average common equity is calculated by taking the net income applicable to common shareholders adjusted for regulatory purposes, and dividing it by the average total common equity, multiplied by 100.

Regulatory Fee: A fee charged users of certain FCC services, such as license applicants and holders, to help support such services.

Re-homing: A network change which involves moving customer services from one switching center to another and establishing the necessary trunking facilities to do so.

Remote Access Server: Equipment at central site that connects remote users with corporate LAN resources.

Remote Alarm Indication (RAI): A code sent upstream in a DSn network as a notification that a failure condition has been declared downstream.

Remote Defect Indication (RDI): A signal returned to the transmitting Terminating Equipment upon detecting a Loss of Signal, Loss of Frame, or AIS defect. RDI was previously known as FERF.

Remote Error Indication (REI): An indication returned to a transmitting node (source) that an errored block has been detected at the receiving node (sink). This indication was formerly known as Far End Block Error (FEBE).

Remote Failure Indication (RFI): A failure is a defect that persists beyond the maximum time allocated to the transmission system protection mechanisms. When this situation occurs, an RFI is sent to the far end and will initiate a protection switch if this function has been enabled.

Repeater: **(1)** A device which serves as an interface between circuits, receiving signals from one circuit and transmitting them to the other. **(2)** A one- or two-way device which amplifies an input signal for retransmission. **(3)** A device that amplifies, reshapes, retimes or performs a combination of these functions on an input pulse for re-transmission.

Repeating Coil: Separates one section of a telephone circuit from another, with no direct current link between the sections.

Request for Comments (RFC): The Internet's Request for Comments documents series. The RFCs are working notes of the Internet research and development community. A document in this series may be on essentially any topic related to computer communication, and may be anything from a meeting report to the specification of a standard.

Request for Discussion (RFD): The part of the newsgroup creation process where you propose a group and discussion starts.

Red, Green Blue (RGB): Method of transmitting video signals that feeds red, green, and blue channels over separate wires; provides highest-quality video signal and is the format for most computer equipment.

Resale: The secondary sale or lease of telecommunications services originally purchased -generally at bulk discount rates - from a carrier, such as Bell Canada. Resellers are usually Bell customers and are entitled to the same provision of company services under the same terms and conditions as any other customer.

Resale Carrier or Reseller: A carrier that does not own transmission facilities, but obtains communications services from another carrier for resale to the public for a profit.

Resale Carrier: A carrier that does not own transmission facilities, but obtains communications services from another carrier for resale to the public for profit.

Reseller - Also known as Rebiller: A long-distance carrier (IEC) that does not own a network, but leases bulk capacity and resells portions of it at a higher rate.

Reset: A modem can be reset. This will change any options (such as parity and speed) to the values that they have when the modem is first used. This can be useful if you change some values for the modem and aren't sure what they do, and then you find that the modem won't work. Resetting the modem will fix everything for you. With Option modems, this is the ATZ command.

Residential Customer: An individual (non-business) telephone system subscriber.

Resolution: A measure of picture resolving capabilities of a television system determined primarily by bandwidth, scan rates and aspect ratio. Relates to fineness of details perceived.

Responsible Organization - R/O - Resporg: With 800 Portability, the Number Administration Service Center (NASC) allows the RespOrg to make changes such as carrier, termination, 800 call routing (by time of day, location.) A Letter Of Agency (LOA) must be on file to change the RespOrg for each customer/account.

Resporg: Responsible Organization, The carrier that has been designated to "be responsible" to ensure a customer's 800 long distance traffic is routed over the correct carrier.

Restoration: Re-establishment of services, usually following the breakdown of a system, on a priority basis.

Retard Coil: A coil having a large inductance which slows sudden changes of the current flow; a choke.

Retrace: The return of a scanning beam to a desired position.

Retrofitting: The installation of additional - equipment or the rebuilding of sections of a system after it has been installed.

Retrieval Engine: A programme which finds and presents data. Same as search engine. Redundant: A backup satellite receive system which would go into operation if the primary system failed. Although the reliability of all electronics has greatly improved, it is desirable to have backup equipment in the receive chain; i.e., a duplicate of each item except the dish. Dual LNA's or BDCs can be mounted on dual feedhorns and could easily be switched in the event of primary system failure. Likewise, two receivers could be operated simultaneously using signal splitters, and either could be switched to the viewing room.

Reuseable Phone Card: A calling card used which can be refilled with units by the addition of funds to the calling card account without the purchase of a new card or a new PIN.

Reverse Billed SMS: A text message that costs money to receive. This is often used as a way for you to pay for something you want.

Reverse Channel: A simultaneous data path in the reverse direction over a half-duplex facility; used for positive/ negative acknowledgements of previously received data blocks.

Ring Network: A local area network in which devices are connected in a closed loop or ring as opposed to a bus network.

Ringback: Signal used by the operator at the receiving end of an established connection to recall an operator at originating end.

Ringdown: A circuit or a method of signaling where the incoming signal is actuated by alternating current over the circuit.

Ringtone: Your phone doesn't have to 'ring ring' it can play a crazy sound or your favourite song.

Riser: Pathway for indoor cables that pass between floors. It is normally a vertical shaft or space.

Rlogin: Lets you log into other computers on the Internet as though you were connected to them directly. "rsh" is a junior version of rlogin.

RLP, Radio Link Protocol: Non-transparent data uses a special ensure robust GSM-specific error correction technique called RLP for transmission. Both MTN and Vodacom GSM networks support both techniques.

Roaming: The use of a wireless phone outside of the "home" service area defined by a service provider. Higher per-minute rates are usually charged for calls made or received while roaming. Long distance rates and a daily access fee may also apply.

Rotary Dial: A mechanism having a 10-hole finger wheel which when wound and released causes pulsing contacts to interrupt the line current and operate the central office selecting equipment in accordance with the digit dialed.

Rotary Hunt: Method in which incoming calls seek out an idle circuit in a prearranged multi-circuit group and find the next open line to establish a through circuit.

Route Optimization: Method for automatic selection of the least costly facility for transmission of a call.

Router Metrics: Algorithms that determine whether one route or path through a network is better than another. Factors include reliability, delay, bandwidth and load.

Router: Device (or in some cases, software) located at network junction points that determines how to send packets of information to a destination. The router is connected to at least two networks so it can forward packets from one network to another. The router decides which way to send data based on what's going on inside the networks.

Routing: Selecting the minimum delay path (and/or minimum cost path) in a network for a message or packet to reach its destination.

Rulemaking Number: A number assigned to a proceeding after the appropriate Bureau/Office has reviewed and accepted a Petition for Rulemaking, but before the Commission has taken action on the petition. The rulemaking number should appear on all appropriate documents, even those which carry a docket number.

Rural Cellular Radio Service Area: A market area not based on Metropolitan Statistical Areas which under existing rules applicants may propose to provide with cellular service, as long as the proposed area does not exceed 2,000 square miles.

S

Sampling Rate/Frequency: The number of samples taken per second of an analog signal, expressed in Hertz. A 44.1KHz sampling rate, used for CD-Audio sound, represents 44,100 samples per second.

Satellite Carrier: An entity that owns or leases the facilities of a satellite or satellite service to establish and operate a channel of communications for point-to-multipoint distribution of television station signals.

Satellite Communications: Satellite communications entails microwave radio, line-of-sight propagation from a transmitting earth terminal (i.e., usually ground-based but potentially ship or airborne) through the atmosphere and outer space media to a satellite, and back to earthbound receiving terminals. In essence, satellites are equivalent to orbiting microwave repeaters.

Satellite Dish: A kind of antenna used to pick up transmissions broadcast from a satellite.

Satellite Earth Terminal: That portion of a satellite link which receives, processes and transmits communications between Earth and a satellite.

Satellite Footprint: In geostationary orbit, communications satellites have direct line-ofsight to almost half the earth - a large "footprint" which is a major advantage. A signal sent via satellite can be transmitted simultaneously to every U.S. city. Multiple downlinks can be aimed at one satellite and receive the same programme; called point to multipoint.

Satellite Master Antenna Television System - SMATV: A system wherein one central antenna is used to receive signals (broadcast or satellite) and deliver them to a concentrated grouping of television sets (such as might be found in apartments, hotels, hospitals, etc.).

Satellite Receiver: A microwave receiver capable of receiving satellite transmitted signals, downconverting, and demodulating those signals, and providing a baseband output. Modern receivers are frequency agile and usually capable of multiple band reception.

Satellite Relay: Active or passive repeater in geosynchronous orbit which amplifies the signal it receives before transmitting it back to earth.

Satellite System: The use of orbiting satellites to relay transmissions from one satellite dish to another or multiple dishes.

Satellite: A radio relay station that orbits the earth. A complete satellite communications system also includes earth stations which communicate with each other via the satellite. The satellite receives a signal transmitted by an originating earth station and retransmits that signal to the destination earth station(s). Satellites are used to transmit telephone, television, and data signals originated by common carriers, broadcasters, and distributors of CATV programme material.

SCA - Subsidiary Communication Authorization: Radio version of vertical blanking intervals (BVI). Public institutions that have access to FM have access to SCA. This electronic technique places the radio signal on the FM spectrum; these signals can only be picked up with special tuners that distinguish the SCA from the FM signals.

Scalability: The ability to vary the information content of a programme by changing the amount of data that is stored, transmitted or displayed. In a video image, this translates into creating larger or smaller windows of video on screens.

Scan-Converter: A device that converts video frequency signals to audio frequencies and vice versa; used in freeze-frame video to transmit video signals over telephone lines.

Scanner: A device for digitizing text, drawings or photographs - anything in paper form. It works like a photocopy machine, but instead of paper, the scanner converts the printed information into digital images. Scanners are used with OCR (optical character recognition) technology, which takes the scanned pages of text and graphs and converts them into the individual letters and words that make up the text and the dots that make up the image, so that the text and images can be edited using a computer.

Scanning: The process of breaking down an image into a series of elements or groups of elements representing light values and transmitting this information in time sequence.

Scenario: In SWAT, a scenario is an iteration of an RFW project. A scenario holds the design detail work units that are associated with the project. A scenario has three different statuses. A Working status indicates that the scenario is under review. A Posted status indicates that a scenario has been identified as the official design. A Final Posted status indicates that a scenario is the "as-built" version of the project.

Scramble: To interfere with an electronic signal or to rearrange its various component parts. In pay television, for example, the signal might be scrambled, and a decoder, also called a descrambler, might be necessary for the signal to be unscrambled so that only authorized subscribers would receive the clear signal.

Scrambler: A device that electronically alters a programme signal so that it can be seen only by persons, typically paid subscribers, with appropriate decoding devices.

Screen Capture: A part of communications software that opens a file on the computer and saves to it whatever scrolls past on the screen while connected to a host system.

Screen Density: The maximum number of accessible screen elements in a video display.

Screen Font: The software that contains the bitmapped images of a particular typeface, at various sizes; used to produce an approximation of the typeface on the screen. Also, a particular size of bitmapped image of a typeface. Also called a bitmap font.

Scrolling: A property of most alphanumeric video display terminals. If the screen of such a video terminal is filled, it will move the entire display image upward, either at a smooth pace or one line at a time, so that room is continuously made at the bottom of the screen for new information.

Seamless Integration: Refers to a situation in which a caller/user does not experience any difficulties or interruptions when their call entails an interconnection between different networks or systems.

Search Engine: A programme which finds and presents data. Same as retrieval engine.

Secondary Channel: Low-speed channel established on a four-wire circuit over which diagnostic or control information is passed.

Section Overhead: Nine bytes of overhead accessed, generated, and processed by section terminating equipment. This overhead supports functions such as framing the signal and performance monitoring.

Section Terminating Equipment (STE): Equipment that terminates the SONET Section layer. STE interprets and modifies or creates the Section Overhead.

Section: The span between two SONET network elements capable of accessing, generating, and processing only SONET Section overhead. This is the lowest layer of the SONET protocol stack with overhead.

Secure Server: A Web server that supports any of the major security protocols, like SSL, that encrypt and decrypt messages to protect them against third party tampering. Making purchases from a secure Web server ensures that a user's payment or personal information can be translated into a secret code that's difficult to crack.

Secure Socket Layer (SSL): Encrypted communications path between two computers. Theoretically protects customer information.

Seek Time: Usually expressed in terms of "average seek time," it provides a comparative number indicating the time required to get from one position to another, in reading a CD-ROM.

Some older CD-ROM drives had seek times in excess of 1,000 milliseconds (ms), or one full second. The newest drives have seek times approaching 200ms.

Selective Addressability - Selectively Addressable Scrambling: The capacity to designate selected receivers to descramble a particular signal. Each decoder has a unique "address." First developed as the pay-per-view option for cable TV, then adopted by satellite networks.

Selective Calling: Ability of a transmitting station to specify which of several stations is to receive a message through the use of assigned codes.

Selective Routing: The capability to route a call to the particular PSAP based on the geographical location from which the call originated. Selective routing is achieved by building telephone number/emergency service number translations in the tandem central office. These translations cause the E9-1-1 database to assign the emergency service number to each telephone number based on the customer's address. Service order activity keeps the E9-1-1 database updated. The E9-1-1 database, in turn, generates recent changes to the tandem office to update the telephone number/ESN translations in the tandem database.

Selective Transfer: Provides the PSAP with the ability to transfer the incoming 9-1-1 call to a fire, police, or ambulance for the particular number calling 9-1-1 by pushing one button. For example, if an incoming 9-1-1 caller was reporting a fire, the PSAP operator would push the fire button on the workstation. The call would go back to the tandem office. In the tandem office, the computer would do a "look-up" for the ESN and automatically route the call to the correct fire department. This differs from fixed transfer, which routes every call to the same fire or rescue number whenever the fire or rescue button is pushed.

Semiconductor: A material whose resistivity lies between that of conductors and insulators, e.g., germanium and silicon. Solid state devices such as transistors, diodes, photocells, and integrated circuits are manufactured from semiconductor materials.

Serial Input/Output: Data transmission in which the bits are sent one by one over a single wire.

Serial Line Interface Protocol (SLIP): Protocol to access the Internet using dial-up connections.

Serial Port: An input/output port of a PC that transmits data one bit at a time.

Serial Transmission: A method of transmitting data in which bits are sent sequentially.

Server Farm: Group of servers housed together in one location for the storage of raw data, Web pages and online functions, or any combination of these. Servers can have individual operating systems or a shared operating system, and may be used when demand is high to balance the load of information requests across a number of servers.

Server: In a network, a server is equipment that makes available file, database, printing, facsimile, communications or other services to client terminals/stations with access to the network. A gateway is a server that permits client terminal/station access to external communications networks and/or information systems.

Service and Equipment Record: List of equipment billed to custon.er by type, quantity, monthly charge, location and billing dates.

Service Group: One or more access lines (DAL or T1) used to terminate calls from one or more 800 service numbers; a group of lines built as one trunk group from a DMS-250 switch.

Service Management System (SMS): In virtual private networks, SMS is a facility used to build and maintain a VPN database allowing customers to programme specific functions for unique business applications. The SMS contains complete specifications of customer defined private network specifications including location data, numbering plan, features, screening actions, authorization codes, calling privileges, etc. This information is downloaded (transmitted) to network control points (NCPs) which implement its instructions on a customer-by-customer basis.

Service Order (SO): A service order is a record that describes a customer request to establish, change, or terminate a service. The service order contains all information required to meet a customer's needs.

Service Plan: The rate plan you select when choosing a wireless phone service. A service plan typically consists of a monthly base rate for access to the system and a fixed amount of minutes per month.

Service Provider (SP): A service provider is an individual, company or organisation that contracts directly with a network operator for premium rate numbers. The service provider is responsible for ensuring that the content and promotion of a service comply with the icstis Code of Practice.

Service Provisioning Measurement Plan (SPMP): Based on monthly interviews with approximately 20,000 customers who have initiated orders for service (e.g., installation or repair) and the work has been completed. Customers are asked if they were satisfied with access to the Business Office/Customer Service Centre, appointment convenience, as well as employee courtesy, helpfulness, professionalism and workmanship. Their reaction is one element in determining whether or not Bell is meeting its quality of service standards. services over unconditioned copper wires at a top speed of 1.544 mbit/s.

Servo: In CD-ROM drives, an electro-mechanical device that uses feedback to achieve precise starts and stops for movements of the optical head and focusing of the laser beam.

Session Layer: Layer 5 of the Open Systems Interconnection (OSI) model, responsible for binding and unbinding logical links between end users and maintaining an orderly dialog between them.

Session: **(1)** Connection between two stations that allows them to communicate. **(2)** Meeting or period devoted to a particular activity.

Severely Errored Second (SES): Severely errored second (SES) - One-second interval where the bit error ratio (BER) exceeds 10-3.

Shared Visual Space: Allows participants to interact with a common graphics display area; e.g., any person can make a change which is seen by all.

Shareware: Software that is freely available on the Internet. If you like and use the software, you should send in the fee requested by the author, whose name and address will be found in a file distributed with the software.

Sharing: The use, by two or more persons, of telecommunications services jointly leased or purchased from a telecommunications carrier.

Shielded Pair: Two insulated wires in a cable wrapped with metallic braid or foil to prevent signal interferences and provide noise-free transmission.

Shielded Twisted Pair: Shielded twisted pair is twisted copper paired wire cable with an outer metallic sheath surrounding insulated conductors.

Short Haul: Circuit designed for use over distances of less than 200 miles.

Shortwave Station: A broadcast station that transmits on frequencies of 6-25 megahertz. These waves are shorter than those sent out by AM stations but longer than those of the Very-High frequency FM radio and television stations.

Shoutdown Line: A point-to-point circuit which permits one station to go off-hook and the conversation is automatically relayed to the distance point; used primarily between single-line telephones which are connected to speakers.

Sideband: Set of frequencies which are produced on either side of the carrier signal as a result of the modulation process.

Signal: A signal is usually a time-dependent value attached to an energy propagating phenomenon used to convey information, for example, an audio or sound signal in which the data is characterized in terms of loudness and pitch.

Signal-to-noise Ratio: Relative power of the signal information to the noise in a specified bandwidth, usually expressed in decibels (dB).

SIM: Subscriber Identity Module. This is a Smart Card installed in every GSM handset. Within the GSM application the three primary roles of the SIM are access control to the network (authentication & ciphering), service personalisation (SMS, advice of charge, etc.), network branding and advertising (graphics printed on SIM card). The new generation of Phase 2+ SIMs will enable services such as virtual cash, mobile banking, ticket reservations etc.

Simple Network Management Protocol (SNMP): SNMP is the application protocol offering network management service in the Internet suite of protocols. A structure for formatting messages and transmitting information between reporting devices (agents) and data collection programmes. Developed jointly by the Department of Defense, industry and the academic community as part of the TCP/IP protocol suite; ratified as an Internet standard in Request for (Comment (RFC) 1098.

Simplex: A circuit capable of transmission in one direction only. Contrast with half duplex and full duplex.

Simtel20: The White Sands Missile Range used to maintain a giant collection of free and low-cost software of all kinds, which was "mirrored" to numerous other ftp sites on the Net. In the fall of 1993, the Air Force decided it had better things to do than maintain a free software library and shut it down.

Simulation: Simulation programmes electronically substitute media for the actual experience, but may be coupled with hands-on devices that help the learner to experience physical movement.

Simultaneous Multiple Round Auction: An auction in which many licenses are put up for auction at the same time. Bidders have the opportunity to top the high bids from the previous round. The auction ends when no bidders are willing to top the bidders from the previous rounds on any of the licenses.

Singing: **(1)** An undesired, self-sustaining whistle or howl in an amplified telephone circuit. **(2)** An occurrence when the sum of the repeater gains exceeds the sum of the circuit losses.

Single Mode Optical Fiber(s): Single mode optical fibers have sufficiently small core diameters in relation to the wavelength (frequency) of operation that electromagnetic (light) wave is constrained to travel in only one transverse path from transmitter to receiver. This requires the utmost in angular alignment of light emitting devices at points where light enters the fiber and results in higher transmitter/termination costs than multimode fiber systems.

Single Channel Per Carrier (SCPC): Signal transmission technique often used in satellite transmission which concentrates one channel of information on a single transmitted carrier for relay through the satellite. The channel may be digital, analog or multiplexed analog in nature provided that its information may be sent on a single narrow band carrier. The Single Channel Per Carrier transmission technique allows multi-channel operation in the satellite with access from any location on the earth.

Single Session: A drive that can read discs on which data was recorded only once, or a CD-ROM on which data was recorded in one pass, either through CD-Recordable technology, or the standard mastering process.

Site: The origination site is the location from which video and/or audio is transmitted and uplinked in a teleconference. Receive transmission from the origination site.

Skew: The angular deviation of recorded binary characters from a line perpendicular to the reference edge of a data medium.

Skewing: Horizontal displacement of video information in bands of approximately 16 lines per field producing a sawtooth effect which is most apparent on vertical picture detail of a television picture originating from the playback of a video tape recording.

Slam: An end user that is PICed without their permission. An RBOC Slam Fee must be paid for each slam.

Slamming Dispute: A situation in which a customer whose long distance service has been changed without their knowledge or without their authorization should call their preferred carrier who can initiate a resolution of the disagreement on their behalf.

Slamming: Customers are "slammed" if their long distance service is changed without their knowledge or without their authorization. The long distance company that "slammed" the customer is assessed a "slamming fee" if it is unable to produce appropriate authorization within 15 days following initiation of a dispute.

Slip: An overflow (deletion) or underflow (repetition) of one frame of a signal in a receiving buffer.

Slope: **(1)** Difference in attenuation of the various frequencies in a band of frequencies; measured in decibels. **(2)** Measurement of the frequency response of a channel.

Slow Scan: Uses transmitters that scan selected frames and transmit the visual information over telephone lines to receive sites where it is reconstituted as a still picture. May refer to still frame video that accepts an image from a camera or other video source one line at a time.

Smart Phone: Wireless telephone equipped with a keyboard that can transmit data as well as voice signals. Smart phones let the users browse the Internet and send and receive e-mail.

Smart Terminal: **(1)** A display unit that can operate in either conversational or block mode and can support a full range of local editing capabilities. **(2)** A computer with communications capabilities.

SMATV: Satellite master antenna television. A distribution system that feeds satellite signals to a hotel, motel, apartment complex, etc.

SMDR: Station message-detail recording - A record of all calls originated or received by a switching system.

Smooth Scrolling: Continuous vertical movement (up or down) of lines of data displayed on a CRT screen, much in the same manner as a credit roll at the end of a movie. Contrast with jump scrolling.

SMPTE Time Code: Society of Motion Picture and Television Engineers' system of giving each frame of video a number to allow indexing and precise tape control. EBU time code is the European Broadcast Union version of SMPTE time code.

SMS Customer Record: All information related to one 800 number, effective date and time, etc.

SMS: Short Message Service will display a pager-like 160 character message in the LCD panel on the phone. Your phone must support SMS.

SMTP - Simple Mail Transfer Protocol: The Internet standard protocol for transferring electronic mail messages from one computer to another. SMTP specifies how two mail systems interact and the format of control messages they exchange to transfer mail.

Snail Mail: Mail that comes through a slot in your front door or a box mounted outside your house.

Snapshot: **(1)** Extract or summary of data taken from a given system. **(2)** Extract passed to another system to complete processing.

SNMP: Simple Network Management Protocol The Internet's standard for remote monitoring and management of hosts, routers and other nodes and devices on a network (RFC 1157).

Snow/Ice on the Satellite Dish: A significant build up of snow (4-5 inches) on the dish can interfere with signal reception. Snow can be removed with a soft broom or soft cloth. Since accurate curvature of the dish is vital to a good signal, avoid banging or hitting the dish. Ladders should not be leaned against the dish as it may warp or change the azimuth and/or elevation setting. A small amount of ice should not cause problems. Software: A set of programmes, procedures or related documentation associated with a system; materials for use with audio visual equipment; programmes in contrast to equipment.

Software: **(1)** Any of the routines, programmes and instructions required to use computers. **(2)** A written statement of the procedures to be used and the format of the data at every step.

Solid State: A class of electronic components utilizing the electronic or magnetic properties of semiconductors.

Sound Board: A device required by a DOS-based computer to access digital sound, exists in the form of an add-in board inserted in the computer, and accesses (and/or creates) .WAV, .SND, MIDI and other digital sound formats.

Source: Terminal or node at which data enters a network.

Space Division: Space division is a switch that implements the switch matrix using a physical, electrical, spatial link. Where older space division switches used electro-mechanical mechanisms with metallic contacts, modern space-division switches are implemented electronically using integrated circuits.

SPE (Synchronous Payload Envelope): The major portion of the SONET frame format used to transport payload and STS path overhead. A SONET structure that carries the payload (service) in a SONET frame or virtual tributary. The STS SPE may begin anywhere in the frame's payload envelope. The VT SPE may begin anywhere in a floating mode VT, but begins at a fixed location in a locked-mode VT.

Speakerphone: Telephone equipped with a speaker and a microphone that allows hands-free conversation.

Special Access Service: A transmission path directly connecting an InterExchange Carrier location in a LATA to an end user premise or another InterExchange Carrier location.

Special Emergency Radio Services (SERS): A Private Land Mobile Radio Service employed by persons or organizations engaged in emergency medical and rescue service, health care, or similar activity.

Special Event Teleconferencing: Teleconference that uses facilities that are temporarily linked for a specific event; implies a temporary satellite network for one-way video and two-way audio.

Special Grade Network Trunk: A trunk conditioned to parameters, by providing amplitude and delay equalization for the purpose of handling special services such as medium-speed data (600 to 2400 bps).

Special Needs Customer: A person who may not have the ability to lift or hold a telephone handset, to dial, to hear another person's voice and the ringing telephone, or to speak at a level which can be heard clearly.

Special Services: Special services are any of a variety of LEC and IXC switched, non-switched, or special rate services that are either separate from public telephone service or contribute to certain aspects of public telephone service. Examples include PBX tie trunks, foreign exchange (FX) and private line services. These services are important to business telecommunication planners/users.

Specialized Carrier: A company that provides value-added communications facilities to limited geographical areas or for specific services.

Specialized Common Carrier (SCC): A company (other than the telephone company) that provides point-to-point communications service on a common carrier basis. For example, point-to-point services are used to connect points on the telephone network that normally cannot be connected using standard wire line or fiber optic because of terrain.

Specialized Mobile Radio Services (SMR): A private, two-way radio system providing land mobile communications service to eligible persons on a commercial basis. Typical SMR customers using dispatch communications include construction companies with several trucks at different jobs or on the road, with a dispatch operation in a central office.

Spectrum: Continuous range of frequencies. The electromagnetic spectrum is a continuum that includes radio waves, visible light and x-rays. The ITU formally recognizes 12 bands, from 30 Hz to 3000 GHz. New bands, from 3 THz to 3000 THz, are under active consideration.

Spectrum Allocation/Management: The assignment of available spectrum space; the coordination of spectrum used to maximize efficiency and to prevent interference.

Spectrum Auction: A public sale of spectrum space in which the price is increased by bids until the highest bidder becomes the purchaser.

Speed Dial: A feature on PBX phones allowing users to dial programmed numbers by simply pressing one button (or entering a two or three digit code).

Speed number: A one-, three- or four-digit number that replaces a seven- or ten-digit telephone number. Numbers programmed into a PBX, the switch in the carrier's office, or individual smart telephones.

Spin Up: Come up to speed. When a CD-ROM is inserted in a drive, it must reach a certain rate of rotational speed in order to be read.

Split Screen: Capability of a CRT screen to be divided into two or more independent workspaces.

Spurious Emission: Any emission or part of it which appears outside of the authorized bandwidth.

SQL: Structured Query Language - commonly used with database servers; powerful language used for the creation, maintenance and viewing of databases.

SS7 (Signaling System 7): Signaling systems monitor the status of a line to see if it is busy or idle; indicate incoming calls (rings, flashing lights, etc.); and transmit routing and destination signals over the network. SS7 is a signaling protocol for digital networks with high-speed circuit-switched connections. It was introduced in the 1980s and is the standard now used by all telecommunications administrators around the world.

SSMA - Spread Spectrum Multiple Access: Frequency modulation technique.

Standard Broadcast Band: The band of frequencies extending from 535 to 1605 kHz, usually called AM.

Standard Industrial Classification (SIC): U.S. government code that categorizes commercial enterprises. [The first two digits place an organization in one of the 13 major groupings; two additional digits show the primary line of business and size.]

Star: A network topology in which each station is connected only to a central station by a point-to-point link; all stations communicate through the central station.

Star Network: A network configuration in which there is only one path between a central or controlling node and each end-point node.

Star-lan: A local network design and specification within IEE 802.3 standards subcommittee; characterized by data transmission over two-pair twisted-pair wiring.

Start Bit: A signal in asynchronous transmission used to signify the beginning of a character or a block of data.

State Tax: A collection of tax types that each state is allowed to charge. Tax jurisdiction (which state can charge tax for a call) is based on the two-out-of-three rule: where it originates, where it terminates, where it is being billed to - if two match, that state can charge the tax.

Station Equipment: Station equipment is a component of telecommunications systems such as a telephone or data terminal, generally located on the user's premises. Its function is to transmit and receive user information (traffic), and to exchange control information with the network to access communications services.

Station message detail recording (SMDR): A computer generated report showing internal usage on a telephone system; usually includes extension number, trunk number used, phone number dialed, time of call, duration and operator involvement.

Station: Any input or output points in a communications system capable of sending or receiving messages or calls.

Station-to-station Call: A call in which the calling party dials the desired telephone number, the call is completed without the assistance of an operator (except under the circumstances described below), and the call is billed automatically to the telephone number from which the call is placed. Under certain circumstances, an operator may be required to complete a station-to-station call. For example, an operator may be needed to record the originating telephone number, where no automatic recording equipment is available or where the caller is disabled and unable to dial the call him/herself. An operator may also be required when a customer-dialed call has been involuntarily interrupted and/or the calling party experiences network difficulty when dialing the call over the telecommunications company's network.

Statistical Multiplexing: A time-division interleaving technique in which timeslots are dynamically allocated on the basis of need or to equipment with data to be transmitted.

Stentor: The Stentor Alliance was formed in 1992 by Canada's leading telecommunications services providers. The Alliance works with customers across Canada to economically deliver leading-edge local, national and international telecommunications services. These companies maintain the world's longest, fully digital, fiber optic network. This network forms the backbone of a Canadian information highway which the Alliance is committed to completing by the year 2005 under the Beacon initiative.

Stereophonic: Giving, relating to, or constituting a three-dimensional effect of auditory perspective, by means of two or more separate signal paths.

Still-Image Video: System by which still images are transmitted over standard telephone lines, usually allowing for real-time interaction between locations.

Storage; memory: A term used to describe any device (generally electronic or magnetic) capable of retaining information.

Store-and-forward: **(1)** Technique in which a message is received from the originator and held in storage until a circuit to the addressee becomes available. **(2)** Transmittal of complete network messages or packets into storage before sending them forward to the next center. **(3)** Capture of transaction data on magnetic media for subsequent batch input to a computer.

Stored Programme Control (SPC): A method whereby instructions are placed in the memory of a common controlled switching unit for use as a reference when processing calls. Instructions may include: class marks, code conversions, routing and trouble analysis.

Strap: Hard-wired connection link between two tags, terminals or items of equipment.

Stratum: Level of clock source used to categorize accuracy.

Streaming: When data is sent continuously, without waiting to make sure there are no errors. Transparent mode on GSM is an example of a streaming method faster than non-transparent mode, but unreliable.

Studio: A specially designed room with associated control and monitoring facilities used by a broadcaster for the origination of radio or television programmes.

Subcarrier: An inaudible portion of the broadcast signal that is added to the programme signal of FM or TV sound and can be used for either broadcast or non-broadcast purposes. Uses include stereo sound, augmented audio for the blind, bilingual programming and paging.

Subscriber Line Charge (SLC): A monthly fee paid by telephone subscribers that is used to compensate the local telephone company for part of the cost of installation and maintenance of the telephone wire, poles, and other facilities that link your home to the telephone network. These wires, poles, and other facilities are referred to as the "local loop." The SLC is one component of access charges.

Subscriber Loop: Circuit between the central office and the customer's premises.

Subscription Television (STV): A special service providing additional programmes in encoded form to television viewers who pay a monthly rate. Devices that attach to the subscriber's set are able to decipher transmitted signals that have been scrambled.

Sunshine Notice/Period: A Public Notice is released seven calendar days before an Open or Closed Commis- sion Meeting, announcing the day and time of the meeting, and listing each item to be considered. The Sunshine Notice is printed in the Federal Register after it is released to the public. The Sunshine Period runs from the time a public notice placing an item on the Sunshine Agenda is released until the text of the decision is issued or a public notice is released stating that the matter has been deleted from the Sunshine Agenda or returned for further consideration. Presentations to decision-making personnel and discussions of the item are generally prohibited during the Period.

Supercomputers: The fastest and most powerful computing systems that are available at any given time.

Supergroup: In frequency division multiplexing (FDM), five channel banks, each containing 12 circuits, combined into a group bank to produce 60 voice channels.

Supermastergroup: In frequency division multiplexing (FDM), 10 group banks are combined to produce 600 voice channels.

Superstation: A television broadcast station, other than a network station, licensed by the FCC that is secondarily transmitted by a satellite carrier.

Supervisory Signals: Supervisory signals are signals used to indicate or control the states of circuits involved in a particular switched connection. A supervisory signal indicates to equipment, to an operator, or to a user that a particular state in the call has been reached and may simplify the need for action.

Supplementary Audio Programme (SAP) : SAP is used to designate that part of the audio signal transmitted with the standard multi-channel sound television broadcast. The multi-channel audio signal contains stereo (left and right), SAP and PRO.

Surcharge: An additional charge on top of a base rate for a specified reason. A fee charged against a calling card usually to cover the phone card company's costs.

Surfing: A slang term used to describe switching a television from channel to channel in a continuous order with a remote control. Also used to describe the process of scanning entries on the Internet.

Surfing the Internet: Skimming across topics on the Internet - moving in and out of systems looking for information that is not specified. More like browsing than a true search. Also net surfing.

Suspense File: An electronic file or folder in which records are kept until errors or problems are resolved.

Switch: An electronic device which opens or closes circuits, changes operating parameters or selects paths either on a space or time division basis.

Switch Matrice: Switch matrices are the mechanism that provides signal paths between its input and output terminations. Modern matrices are electronic and involve either time or space division switching. A time division switch employs a TDM process, in a time-slot interchange (TSI) arrangement. In space division, a physical, electrical, spatial link is established through the switch matrix. Whereas older space division switches used electro-mechanical mechanisms with metallic contacts, modern space-division switches are implemented electronically using integrated circuits.

Switchboard: Equipment used to manually interconnect lines and trunks. A manually-operated switching position which is part of a Private Branch Exchange (PBX) service furnished to a customer and is used to control the interconnection of lines and trunks.

Switched 56/64 kbps Data Transmission: Provides users with the end-to-end capability to transport high-speed data (up to 64 kbps) over the public network.

Switched Access: Long distance carrier access method in which a non-local call is carried by a local exchange carrier via a Central Office trunk for the first and last part of the call's journey and on the long distance carrier's network only for the middle part of the journey. Also called "switched to switched" or "off-net to off-net."

Switched Circuit: A circuit that may be temporarily established at the request of one or more stations.

Switched Line: One of a series of lines that can be interconnected to all other lines through a switching center; a line on the public telephone network. Contrast with leased line.

Switched Message Network: Any network service providing interconnection of message devices such as teletypewriters.

Switched Network: Any network in which switching is present and is used to direct messages from the sender to the ultimate recipient. Usually switching is accomplished by disconnecting and reconnecting lines in different configurations in order to set up a continuous pathway between the sender and the recipient.

Switched Resellers: Resellers that utilize their own switching hardware (and sometimes their own lines) and the lines of other IXCs to provide long-distance service to its subscribers. They provide their own billing and service.

Switched System: A communications system (such as a telephone system) in which arbitrary pairs or sets of terminals can be connected together by means of switched communications lines.

Switching: Switching refers to the process of connecting appropriate lines and/or trunks to form a desired communications path between two station sets, or more generally, any two arbitrary points in a telecommunications network. Included are all kinds of related functions such as signaling, monitoring the status of circuits, translating address to routing instructions, alternate routing, testing circuits for busy conditions, and detecting and recording troubles.

Switching Center: Location where an incoming call/message is automatically or manually directed to one or more outgoing circuits.

Switching Entity; switching Unit: A single switching machine. One or more switching units constitutes a switching centre.

Switching Fee: per-line fee (usually around 5$) imposed by the LEC to reprogramme their switching system to change your default carrier. Subscribers must usually pay this fee when switching to a reseller.

Switching Office: Telephone company location housing a switch.

Switching Systems: Switching systems are interconnect transmission facilities at various network locations and route traffic through a network.

Switchless Reseller: A reseller of long-distance services that does not utilize any of its own lines, or (switching) equipment. All actual service and equipment is handled by the IXC. Billing is usually done, by the reseller themselves, to the customer.

Symmetrical Compression: A compression system that requires equal processing capability for compression and decompression of an image. Used in applications where both compression and decompression will be utilized frequently. Examples include stillimage databasing, still-image transmission (color fax), video production, video mail, videophones and videoconferencing. Asymmetrical Compression requires more processing capability to compress an image than to decompress an image.

Synchronization: Process of adjusting a receiving terminal or switch clock to match the transmitting system's master clock.

Synchronous: Having a constant time interval between successive bits, characters or events.

Synchronous Communication: Communication which takes place in the same time frame. Examples are live teleconferences which must be viewed when they are broadcast. If the teleconference is taped and viewed later, it becomes asynchronous communication - communication which takes place at the convenience of the end user through the technology of video tape recording.

Synchronous Time-Division Multiplexing: Assigning time slots to devices on a shared network on a fixed, pre-determined basis.

Synchronous Transmission: Data characters and bits are transmitted at a fixed rate with the transmitter and receiver synchronized. This eliminates the need for start-stop elements, thus providing greater efficiency.

Syndicated Exclusivity (SYNDEX) Rule: This rule requires cable systems carrying distant signals to black out syndicated programming (usually on superstations) for which a local broadcaster owns exclusive rights.

Syntax Error: System response to a mistake in its instructions, such as a transposition of characters or an omission of a character or word.

Syntax: Rules governing structure in a programming language.

Sysadmin: The system administrator; the person who runs a host system or publicaccess site.

Sysop - A System Operator: Somebody who runs a bulletin board system or network; responsible for keeping the network or BBS working properly.

System Design: Specifications of the working relations between all the parts of a system in terms of their characteristic actions.

System Reliability: Probability that a system will perform its specified task properly under stated conditions of environment.

System: A set of equipment or apparatus which is combined to perform a function within a carrier's telecommunications network.

Systems Network Architecture (SNA): SNA is IBM's proprietary description of the logical structure, formats, protocols, and operational sequences for transmitting information units through and controlling network configuration and operation.

T

T1 (DS-1) Channel: High-speed digital data channel/carrier with a bit rate of 1.544 mbps which requires a bandwidth of approximately 2.1616 MHz to transmit in a television type cable environment: (1.4 x 1.544 = 2.1616); a general term for a digital carrier (DS-1. available for high-volume voice or data traffic; often used for compressed video teleconferencing networks. Each T1 circuit can accommodate 24 voice channels. A video codec operating at the T1 rate uses the equivalent of 24 voice channels. A codec operating at 56 or 64 Kbps is operating in the range of one voice channel. A standard video signal digitized at 90 Mbps has approximately 1400 voice channels. The compressed video signal quality and the cost decreases as the transmission speed decreases.

T1 Carrier: A T1 carrier is a time-division multiplexed digital transmission facility capable of supporting 24 voice channels, (each encoded as a 64 kbps PCM DS0 signal), producing an aggregate multiplexer output signal at the 1.544 Mbps DS1 rate. Developed in the 1960s, the T1 carrier is designed to operate full duplex over two pairs in unshielded twisted pair (UTP) cable.

T1 Line: High-capacity circuit capable of carrying 24 phone lines over two unshielded, twisted pairs. A T1 digital transmission line (sometimes known as a Digital Signal Level 1 or D1 line) operates at a nominal bandwidth of 1.544 Mpbs.

Table Driven: A logical computer process in which a user-entered variable is matched against an array of predefined values.

Frequently used logical process in network routing, access security and modem operation.

Tail End Hop Off (TEHO): Call in a private network which is carried over flat rate facilities (intermachine trunks or IMTs) to the switching node closest to its destination and is connected into the public network as a local call.

Talk-back Circuit: An audio return link from a receive location to the originating video/audio point. The equipment used is generally either a leased telephone line, dedicated radio link, or special microwave equipment made for this service.

Tandem Office: Telephone central office which serves a tandem area for all 9-1-1 calls. It must be a 1AESS type of central office. The tandem office translations contain the telephone number/ESN which route the 9-1-1 call to the proper PSAP. The tandem office looks up the ANI that it receives from the end office and finds the emergency service number (routing information) which corresponds to a PSAP.

Tandem Switching System: A tandem switching system is a broad functional category describing systems that connect trunks to trunks, and route traffic through a network.

Tandem Switching: The use of an intermediate switch or switches to interconnect circuits from the switch of one serving central office to the switch of a second serving central office in the same exchange.

Tandem Tie Trunk Network (TTTN): A serving arrangement which permits sequential connection of a group of private lines between PBX or CENTREX locations by utilizing a tandem switching operation.

Tandem Trunking: Group of lines which connect two or more switches together.

Tandem: A switching arrangement in which the trunk from the calling office is connected to a trunk at the called office through an intermediate point; serves to interconnect central offices when direct interoffice trunks are not available.

Tariff: A tariff is a published rate for a specific telecommunications service, equipment, or facility that constitutes a public contract between the user and the telecommunications supplier (i.e., carrier); tariff services and rates are established by and for telecommunications common carriers in a formal process in which carriers submit filings for federal or state government regulatory review, public comments, possible amendment, and approval.

TBC - Time Base Corrector: An electronic accessory to a videotape recorder that helps make mixed format playback or transfers electronically stable. It helps maintain picture quality even in dubbing operations within a single tape format.

TCP/IP (Transmission Control Protocol/Internet Protocol): Suite of protocols developed in the 1970s by the U.S. Department of Defense to support construction of worldwide networks. Every computer with access to the Internet has a TCP/IP programme that allows it to communicate with every other computer on the Internet.

TDMA - Time Division Multiple Access: Form of multiple access where a single carrier is time shared by many users. Signals from earth stations reaching the satellite consecutively are processed in time segments without overlapping.

Technical Operating Center (TOC): Telco location where telecommunications operations and equipment are tested and monitored; each center contains wire centers, test jacks, equipment racks, mux and radio equipment. [TOC operations include circuit installation, circuit maintenance and performance monitoring. Some, but not all TOCs, are equipped with switch equipment.]

Telco - Telephone Company: The local or regional telephone company that owns and operates lines to customer locations and Class 5 Central Office Switches. Telcos have connections to other COs, Tandem (Class 4 Toll) offices and may connect directly to IECs like WorldCom, AT&T, MCI, Sprint, LDDS, etc.

Telecommunication Lines: Circuits, trunks, cables and other links that are used to transmit messages from one location to another.

Telecommunication(s): This word has no precise definition, but is frequently used. Its definition ranges from "any form of communication over a distance" to "any communication by electric means" to "two computers talking to each other via modems." Methods of communications that probably are considered telecommunications: telephones, cellphones, TV's and fax machines. The word is used both in singular and plural.

Telecommunications Act of 1996: A bill signed in order to "promote competition and reduce regulation in order to secure lower prices and higher quality services for American telecommunications consumers and encourage rapid deployment of new telecommunications technologies." This act required local service providers in the 100 largest metropolitan areas to implement local number portability by the end of 1998, enabling the CLECs to better compete. It also allowed local RBOCs into long distance service once they had met certain conditions about competition in their local monopoly areas. In addition, the goal of universal service to all Americans was introduced, with special considerations established to address the telecommunications needs of schools, libraries, and rural health care providers.

Telecommunications Closet: Enclosed space for housing telecommunications equipment, cable terminations and cross-connects. The closet is the recognized cross-connect between the backbone and horizontal cabling.

Telecommunications Common Carrier (TCC): Person, firm or corporation that owns or operates telecommunications facilities for the purpose of providing either the facilities or services for profit.

Telecommunications Infrastructure: The underlying structure or framework of the telecommunications system (i.e., cable, switching equipment, amplifiers, etc.) which allows for the transmission of voice, video and data.

Telecommunications Network: A telecommunications network is a system of interconnected facilities designed to carry traffic from a variety of telecommunications services. The network has two different but related aspects. In terms of its physical components, it is a facilities network. In terms of the variety of telecommunications services that it provides, it can support a set of many traffic networks, each representing a particular interconnection of facilities.

Telecommunications Relay Service (trs): A free service that enables persons with TTYs, individuals who use sign language and people who have speech disabilities to use telephone services by having a third party transmit and translate the call.

Telecommunications Service: Telecommunications service is a specified set of information transfer capabilities provided to a group of users by a telecommunications system.

Telecommunications System: A collection of individual communications networks, transmission systems, relay stations, tributary stations, and data terminal equipment (DTE) usually capable of interconnection and interoperation to form an integrated whole. Note: The components of a communications system serve a common purpose, are technically compatible, use common procedures, respond to controls, and operate in unison.

Telecommunications: Telecommunications is any process that enables one or more users to pass to one or more other users information of any nature delivered in any usable form, by wire, radio, visual, or other electrical, electromagnetic, optical means. The word is derived from the Greek tele, "far off," and the Latin communicare "to share."

Telecommuter - telecommuting: Ability to work from home, local office, or from the road because of equipment. Equipment allows the telecommuting employee to work from anywhere. The equipment includes a telephone, fax, modem and as the NII is deployed, video.

Telecommuting: The idea of company employees working from home, rather than their office. At home, they can communicate with the office (and other entities) by modem or voice calls.

Telecomputer: Equipment used to receive digitized information in audio, video, and data modes.

Teleconference: Electronic communications between two or more groups, or three or more individuals, who are in separate locations via audio, audiographics, video or computer. Audio teleconference - two-way communication between two or more groups, or three or more individuals, in separate locations. Video teleconference - one (or more) uplink and downlink sites. May be fully interactive voice and video, two-way voice and one-way video; full-motion, compressed, or freeze-frame video.

Tele-Direct (Services) Inc.: Tele-Direct (Services) Inc. provides directory publishing services to Canadian telephone companies, such as New Brunswick Telephone Company Limited (NBTel) Newfoundland Telephone Company Limited, NorthwesTel and more than 40 independent telephone companies across Canada.

Tele-Direct International: Tele-Direct International, through its affiliates, provides directory publishing services to telephone companies around the world including Hong Kong, the Middle East, India and the Caribbean.

Telegraph: A device which interrupts or changes the polarity of DC current signaling to convey coded information.

Telegraphy: System of communicating coded information by the transmission of electrical signals generated by a telegraph key.

Telemanagement: The management of a company's telephone and telecommunications systems, from call accounting to corporate inventory management.

Telemarketing: A systematic, controlled and purposeful programme in which the telephone is used as a marketing tool to seek and maintain customers.

Telemetry: Transmission of a measurement over long distances, usually by electromagnetic means. Includes the apparatus for measuring, formulating and recording the value of a measured quantity at a distance. For example water level monitoring or flow-rate metering.

Telenet: A public packet-switching network operated by US Sprint. Also known as "SprintNet".

Telephone Conference Bridge: Device that links three or more telephone channels for a teleconference; usually refers to a bridge that provides only dial-up teleconferencing where an operator calls each participant. Contrast to meet-me bridge.

Telephone: A device used mainly for voice communications which converts audible signals into electrical waves, which can then be transmitted over communications channels.

Telephony: The science of translating sound into electrical signals, transmitting the signals, and then converting the electrical signals back to sound.

Telesat Canada: Established in 1969, Telesat Canada operates a commercial satellite communications system throughout Canada.

Teletype: **(1)** Trademark of the Teletype Corporation. **(2)** Frequently used as a generic name for keyboard/printers and for asynchronous transmission.

Teletypewriter: Machine used to transmit and/or receive communications on a printed page and/or tape.

Television Receive Only Earth Station (TVRO): Earth station equipment that receives video signals from satellite or MDS-type transmissions. Such stations have only receiving capability and need not be licensed by the FCC unless the owner wants protec-tion from interference. Authority for reception and use of material transmitted must be given by the sender.

Telewriter: General term for an electronic device that produces free-hand information that can be sent over a telecommunications channel, usually a telephone line.

Telex Service: A public switched service in which teletypewriter stations are provided with lines to a central office for access to other stations.

Telkom (South Africa): Telkom is the parastatal fixed-line network operator in South Africa. Option modems are approved for use on the telkom network and 25 other networks around the world.

Telnet: The Internet standard protocol for remote terminal connection service. Allows a user at one site to interact with a remote time sharing system at another site as if the user's terminal was connected directly to the remote computer. On the Macintosh, NCSA Telnet is the standard.

Terminal - (1) A point at which information can enter or leave a communications network. **(2)** A device for the input or output of data.

Terminal Emulation: When a communications programme can simulate the operations of a smart terminal.

Terminal Equipment: Devices, apparatuses and associated interfaces used to forward information to a local customer or distant point.

Terminal: 1. Generally, connection point of equipment, power or signal. 2. Any terminating piece of equipment such as a computer terminal.

Terminating Communications Provider (TCP): Also known as 'Terminating Networks', A TCP is the network at which your call will end its journey and connect to the service you are paying for. TCP's do not usually have public customers, their customers are OCP's and service providers.

Termination Gateway: The computer equipment configured with certain hardware and software, which provides the electronic "bridge" from an IP network to the PSTN to connect to the destination telephone.

Termination: (1) Item such as a port that is connected to the end point of a circuit or equipment. **(2)** The points on a switching network to which a trunk or line may be attached.

Terrestrial Carrier/Land Line: Telecommunications transmission system using landbased facilities (microwave towers, telephone lines, fiber optic cable).

Terrestrial Microwave Radio: Terrestrial microwave radio is a transmission systems consisting of at least two radio transmitter/receivers (transceivers) connected to high gain antennas (directional antennas which concentrate electromagnetic or radiowave energy in narrow beams) focused in pairs on each other. The operation is point-to-point, that is, communications are established between two and only two antennas (installations) with line-of-sight visibility. This can be contrasted to point-to-multipoint systems like broadcast radio or television.

Test Jack Frame (TJF): A frame supplied by the PABX supplier providing a connection point for the exchange line and extension ports to the BDF. It acts as a demarcation point between these.

Test Marketing: Research conducted within a small targeted consumer group to determine the viability of an expanded programme.

Test Period: A defined amount of time used to measure circuit performance prior to releasing the circuit to a customer, usually after initial installation.

Text Telephone (TT): A machine that employs graphic communication in the transmission of coded signals through a wire or radio communication system. TT supersedes the term "TDD" or "telecommunications device for the deaf."

Text: In terms of files, a file that contains only characters from the ASCII character set. In terms of FTP, a mode that assumes that files will be transferred containing only ASCII characters.

Thicknet - Thinnet: Thicknet cable can support longer distances than Thinnet (500 meters) and have up to 100 nodes connected to it. Thinnet cable looks similar to television cable and is often used to connect networks within limited distances (185 meters) and limited nodes (35).

Third Generation 3G: The next generation Cellular Radio for mobile telephony. Due to come on stream from 2001 onwards, 3G will be the first cellular radio technology designed from the outset to support wideband data communications just as well as it supports voice communications. It will be the basis for a wireless information society where access to information and information services such as electronic commerce is available anytime, anyplace and anywhere to anybody.

Third-Generation Cellular (3G): Proposed new cellular standard that promises increased capacity and high-speed data applications. The third generation of wireless technology, with the ability to handle broadband data communications, will feature receiving speeds significantly higher than today's 10 kbps, with global roaming.

Third-party billing; third-number billing: A procedure whereby long distance calls can be charged to a telephone number different from that of either the calling party or the called party (e.g., a home or office number).

Thread: A group of messages in a Usenet discussion group that all share the same subject and topic, so one can easily read the entire thread or delete it, depending on the specific newsreader.

Tie-line: A private line communications channel provided by communications common carriers that links two or more points together.

Time Code: Code electronically placed on a videotape that appears on the screen or on a counter to locate specific footage and edit tape. Logs are made of the footage on tape before editing so it can be located and viewed quickly during the editing.

Time Division Multiple Access/TDMA: Code Division Multiple Acess /CDMA These terms are used to describe multiple access systems. For example, CDMA is a method of spreading spectrum transmission for digital wireless personal communications networks that allows a large number of users simultaneously to access a single radio frequency band without interference. TDMA is a method of digital transmission for wireless telecommunications systems that allows a large number of users simultaneously to access a single radio frequency band without interference.

Time Division Multiplexing (TDM): Time Division Multiplexing is a transmission facility shared in time (rather than frequency), i.e., signals from several sources share a single channel or bus by using the channel or bus in successive time slots. A discrete time slot or interval is assigned to each signal source.

Time Division Switch: A time division switch is a switch that implements the switch matrix using the TDM process, in a time-slot interchange (TSI) arrangement (usually denoted by T in combined time and space division switches).

Time Sharing: Pertaining to the interleaved use of time on a computer system that enables two or more users to execute computer programmes concurrently.

Token Bus: Local network access mechanism and topology in which all stations actively attached to the bus listen for a broadcast token or supervisory frame. Stations wishing to transmit must receive the token before doing so; however, the next physical station to transmit is not necessarily the next physical station on the bus. Bus access is controlled by preassigned priority algorithms.

Token Passing: Local area network access technique in which participating stations circulate a special bit patter (the token) that grants network access to each station in sequence; often used in networks with a ring topology.

Token Ring: Local network access and topology in which a supervisory frame or token is passed from station to station in sequential order. Stations wishing to gain access to the network must wait for the token to arrive before transmitting data. In a token ring, the next logical station receiving the token is also the next physical station on the ring.

Toll Call: Any transmission on the public switched network to a point outside the local service area.

Toll Center: Central office where operators (human or mechanical) are present to assist in completing incoming toll calls.

Toll Office: Switching center where inter-city circuits terminate; usually one switching center in a city is designated as the toll office and is also used for mileage rate measurements.

Toll Restriction: Arrangement by which some telephone lines are denied access to long distance circuits.

TOPS (Traffic Operator Position System): A work station and the associated electronic switching system that permit the processing of operator-handled calls (e.g., "0" plus, automatic coin rating and hotel/motel requirements).

Touch Sensitive: System which identifies physical contact on a screen by coordinates and transmits the information to a computer to be translated into some system action.

Touchtone Adapter: Device that can be connected to a rotary dial telephone to allow for dual tone multifrequency tone (DTMF) signaling.

Touchtone: **(1)** Refers to DTMF signaling equipment. **(2)** Frequently used to describe telephone equipment with pushbuttons.

Tracking: Tracking features user-defined approval levels and project milestone tables to generate project cost and status information, which is tracked for reporting and review. As assigned tasks are completed, supervisors make daily entries identifying the number of hours worked on a task, materials used, and the number of work units completed. This information is then available for project jeopardy tracking, cost tracking, and determination of contractor payments due.

Traffic Measurement and Recording Systems (TMRS): A computer-generated report with usage information of telephone systems; usually includes trunk utilization, outages, queuing time and the need for additional common equipment.

Transceiver: A transceiver is a generic term describing a device that can both transmit and receive. In IEEE 802 local area network (LAN) standards, a transceiver consists of a transmitter, receiver, power converter, and, for CSMA/CD LANs, collision detector and jabber detector capabilities. The transmitter receives signals from an attached terminal's network interface card (NIC) and transmits them to the coaxial cable or other LAN medium. The receiver receives signals from the medium and transmits them via the transceiver cable and NIC to the attached terminal. The jabber detector is a timer circuit that protects the LAN from a continuously transmitting terminal.

Transfer Mode: Transfer mode is a generic term for switching and multiplexing aspects of broadband integrated services digital networks (BISDN), adopted by CCITT Study Group XVIII.

Transfer Rate: The amount of data that can be communicated from the CD-ROM drive to the CPU. Standard CD-ROM data transfer rate is 155KB/sec, (often rounded to 150KB/sec).

Translator: A television or FM broadcast station, operating at relatively low power, that receives a corresponding television or FM signal on one channel, amplifies it, and retransmits it on another channel.

Transmission Channel: The medium by which a signal is sent and received between separate locations.

Transmission Control Protocol/Internet Protocol (TCP/IP): Collective name for the set of protocols on which the Internet is based. TCP and IP are the best known of this set, but they are by no means the only ones. TCP guarantees that every byte sent from one port arrives at the other in the same order and without duplication or loss. IP assigns local IP addresses to physical network addresses providing a structure which can be recognised by Routers. Other members of the TCP/IP family include the Telnet protocol which allows a remote terminal to log in to another host, the Domain Name System (DNS) which allows users to refer to hosts by name rather than having to know their numeric IP addresses, the File Transfer Protocol (FTP) which defines a mechanism for storing and retrieving files, and HyperText Transfer Protocol (HTTP) which allows information to be transferred from host computers to computers equipped with web browsers.

Transmission Facilities: Transmission facilities provide the communication paths that carry user and network control information between nodes in a network. In general, transmission facilities consist of a medium and electronic equipment located at points along the medium. This equipment amplifies (analog systems) or regenerates (digital systems) signals, provides termination functions at points where transmission facilities connect to switching systems, and may provide the means to combine many separate sets of call information into a single "multiplexed" signal to enhance the transmission efficiency.

Transmission Impairments: Transmission impairments is the degradation caused by practical limitations of channels, or interference induced from outside the channel.

Transmission Medium: Transmission medium is any material substance or "free space" (i.e., a vacuum) that can be, or is, used for the propagation of suitable signals, usually in the form of electromagnetic (including light waves), or acoustic waves, from one point to another; unguided in the case of free space or gaseous media or guided by a boundary of material substance.

Transmission Speed: Number of pulses or bits transmitted in a given period of time, usually expressed as bits per second (bps) or words per minute (wpm).

Transmission System: Facilities used for the transfer of information from one geographic location to another. An information transmission medium generally consists of copper conductors, fiber or microwave radio.

Transmission: The electrical transfer of a signal, message or other form of data from one location to another without unacceptable loss of information content due to attenuation, distortion or noise.

Transmit Level: The "loudness" level of the sound leaving a modem to go over the phone lines. It is measured indBm's. It should be different at different frequencies, since certain frequencies have more loss over the phone line than others.

Transparent Data Transmission: A method of transmission in which the transmission medium will not recognize control characters or initiate any control function. Transparent-based phones do not utilise any error correction. Thus the data sent and received MIGHT be corrupted unless a greater than two-bar cellphone signal is used. Non-transparent data uses a special ensure robust GSM-specific error correction technique called RLP for transmission. Both MTN and Vodacom GSM networks support both techniques.

Transponder - Channel - Downlink Frequency: A satellite microwave repeater (receiver and transmitter) receives the signal from an uplink, amplifies it, down converts the frequency of a received band of signals, and re-transmits the signal back to earth. Satellites have 12, 24, or more transponders each with the capacity for one color TV signal and two audio channels. Typically transponder with 24 transponders have twelve polarized for vertical and twelve for horizontal transmissions in order to optimize the bandwidth of the satellite and the respective transponders.

Transponder: The device in a communications satellite that receives signals from the earth, translates and amplifies them on another frequency, and retransmits them.

Transport Layer: In the OSI model, the network processing entity responsible for the end-to-end control of transmitted data and the optimized use of network resources; works in conjunction with the underlying network, data, link and physical layers.

Transport Services: Transport Services are network switching, transmission and related services that support information transfer capabilities between originating and terminating access service facilities.

Treatment: A narrative description of a media programme. In videoteleconferencing, usually describes routine of action and precedes a rundown and/or script.

Tree: Type of bus topology in which the network branches out at certain points along its length to connect stations or clusters of stations; also called a branching bus.

Truncation: **(1)** Removal of one or more digits, characters or bits from one end of a block of data when a string length or target variable has been exceeded. **(2)** To cut off at a specified spot.

Trunk: **(1)** Group of circuits that carry call traffic in and out of the switch. **(2)** Circuit or channel connecting two exchanges or two switching devices. **(3)** Circuit capable of being switched at both ends and provided with the necessary terminating and signaling equipment.

Trunk-side Access: A circuit that is connected to the "trunk side" of a local telephone switch. This type of access is provided to alternate providers of long distance service so that their customers can make long distance calls without dialing extra digits.

Tuner: A device, circuit, or portion of a circuit that is used to select one signal from a number of signals in a given frequency range.

TVRO - Television Receive Only: Earth stations which receive (but not transmit) satellite transmissions. Normally comprised of a parabolic antenna, low noise converted (LNC) or low noise amplifier (LNA) and a satellite receiver. The antenna gathers the weak signals transmitted from the communications satellite located in the geostationary orbit which are then amplified and downconverted to a more usable portion of the spectrum by the low noise converted. From the LNC the signals may travel up to several hundred feet to a satellite receiver; the output of which is typically video and audio or modulated channel three or four. 23B+D The capability of ISDN primary rate interface (PRI) to enable data terminals served by a DMS-100 ISDN node to have fully digital circuit- and packet-switched ISDN internetworking with data terminals served by PBXs.

Twisted Pair: Pair of insulated metal wires twisted together but not covered with an outer sheath. The term also denotes those segments of intra-building communications wiring arrangements that are not microwave radio channels, main telephone cables, coaxial cables or fiber optic cables.

Two Out Of Three Rule: When determining state tax jurisdiction, there are three locations to consider: originating station, destination station, and the location that the bill is sent to. If two out of three are the same, then that state receives the tax.

Two-way Cable TV Capability: Interactive services offered by cable systems, for example, home shopping, banking and polling services.

Two-way Circuit: **(1)** A circuit in which information signals in both directions are carried by the same two-wire path. **(2)** A short-distance channel using a single send/receive pathway, usually two copper wires, connecting a telephone to a switch.

Two-Wire Circuit: A typical telephone circuit on the public switched network; a circuit formed by two conductors insulated from each other to provide a send and receive channel in the same frequency.

Type Family: A collection of related typefaces, designed to work together attractively. Also used to mean the collection of weights and styles of a single typeface.

Ultra High Frequency (UHF): The part of the radio spectrum from 300 to 3000 megahertz which includes TV channels 14-83, as well as many land mobile and satellite services.

U

Umbrella Prices: Refers to regulated prices for services (e.g., long distance) that are offered by telephone companies at levels high enough to allow competitors to enter the market uneconomically and charge lower prices.

Unattended Operation: Transmission and/or reception that is controlled automatically and does not require a human operator.

Unbundling: Unbundling is the term used to describe the access provided by local exchange carriers so that other service providers may buy or lease portions of its network elements, such as interconnection loops to serve subscribers.

Uneconomic Entry: Refers to a situation in which an industry's long-term unit costs of producing a good or service increase because entry from competitors occurs. For example, when the prices of services are artificially maintained above their costs to cross-subsidize local service, an entrant could undercut the existing price, yet have higher unit costs than the telephone companies. This would result in an increase in industry unit costs.

Unguided Media: Unguided media is any medium in which boundary effects between "free space" and material substances are absent. The "free space" medium may or may not include a gas or vapor. Unguided media including the earth's atmosphere and outer space support terrestrial and satellite radio and optical transmission.

Uniform Call Distributor (UCD): Device located at the telephone office or with a PABX which distributes incoming calls evenly among stations or agents.

Uniform Service Order Code (USOC): Information encoded for billing purposes by the local telephone company; typically used on service orders and service equipment records.

Uniformed Resource Locator (URL): The standard way to give the address of any resource that is on the Internet and is part of the World Wide Web. For example, the FCC's URL is http://www.fcc.gov

Uninterruptible Power Supply (UPS): Equipment providing no break power supply for the duration of the reserves of its batteries in the event of failure of the primary source of power.

Unions: The unions most closely associated with video production. Usually, if one group of people on a production are union, all will be. They may belong to the following unions:Actors Equity represents actors in certain areas of the country.

Unipolar: **(1)** Neutral transmission of teletypewriter signals, where current indicates a mark and no current means a space signal. **(2)** Logical opposites are represented by the same electrical voltage polarity.

Universal Service: The financial mechanism which helps compensate telephone companies or other communications entities for providing access to telecommunications services at reasonable and affordable rates throughout the country, including rural, insular and high costs areas, and to public institutions. Companies, not consumers, are required by law to contribute to this fund. The law does not prohibit companies from passing this charge on to customers.

UNIX: An operating system developed by Bell Laboratories that supports multiuser and multitasking operations.

Unshielded Twisted Pair (UTP): UTP is a two wood pulp or plastic insulated copper conductors (wires), twisted together into pairs, capable of propagating electromagnetic waves. The twists, or lays, are varied in length to reduce the potential for signal interference between pairs, in multi-pair cables. Wire sizes range from 26 to 19 gauge (i.e., 0.016 to 0.036 inch in diameter) and are typically manufactured in cables of from 2 to 3600 pairs. Shielded twisted pair cable is similar to UTP, but the twisted pairs are surrounded by a cylindrical metallic conductor that is clad with an insulating sheath.

Upgrouping: Occurs when the telephone count in an exchange (i.e., the number of phones that can be reached toll-free, times a weighting factor) outgrows its current rate group and moves it to the next highest local rate group. Each rate group has a minimum and a maximum number of permitted telephone lines which determines the basic local rate customers pay for telephone service.

Uplink: An earth station that transmits a radio frequency signal to a communications satellite. The transmitting facility, or uplink, consists of a large dish-shaped antenna and high-power amplifiers. The uplink is like the transmitter of a radio or television station, except that it concentrates it signals in one direction by means of a parabolic dish antenna that delivers a strong pinpoint signal to a specific satellite in space.

Upload: Copy a file from your computer to a host system. Upload is the term used for sending information over a network. Download refers to receiving information off a network. To save on connect time charges users often download information on to a data disk, and then work with it off-line.

UPS (Uninterruptible Power Supply): System for delivering a steady source of electricity to communications equipment. UPS systems may be a bank of batteries or a standby generator with sufficient fuel storage for continuous operation over several days.

URL - Uniform Resource Locator: A standard for writing a text reference to an arbitrary piece of data in the WWW. A URL looks like "protocol://host/localinfo" where protocol specifies a protocol to use to fetch the object (like HTTP or FTP), host specifies the Internet name of the host on which to find it, and local info is a string (often a file name) passed to the protocol handler on the remote host.

Usage: (1) Measure of trunk or equipment occupancy in telephone traffic engineering. [One trunk busy for an hour carries one erlang of traffic. Usage is measured in CCSs (hundred-call seconds) where 36 CCS per hours = one erlang.].

Usenet Groups: Usenet groups are also known as newsgroups, or discussion groups. Users exchange information generally provided in a "chat room."

User Class of Service: A category of data transmission provided in a network in which the data signaling rate and terminal operating mode are standardized.

User Datagram Protocol (UDP): A protocol similar to TCP; however, it does not check data at the receiving end to ensure that all the packets have arrived, and doesn't re-send missing data.

User Name: A short name (with no spaces allowed) unique to you on your Internet access provider's system. Sometimes these are assigned and sometimes you can select your own. The user name, or ID, followed by your site address, becomes your e-mail address. For example, if Ben Franklin had an account at world.std.com and he chose a user name of bfranklin, his e-mail address would be bfranklin@world.std.com.

UUCP - Unix-to-Unix Copy Programme: A method for transferring Usenet postings and e-mail that requires far fewer Net resources than TCP/IP, but which can result in considerably slower transfer times.

Value added network (VAN): A public data communications network that provides basic transmission facilities (generally leased by the VAN vendor from a common carrier) plus additional, enhanced services such as computerized switching, temporary data storage, error detection and correction, electronic mail service and packet switching.

V

Value Added Reseller (VAR): Company offering services other than the core service. For example, a company who sells computers and offers training, service, and on-going maintenance is considered a VAR.

Vector Quantization: Compression coding technique that uses block processing to exploit redundancies within a frame. For example, if the blue sky background within a frame is one constant color, one pixel of that color is all that needs to be stored.

Veronica: An information agent that searches a database of Gopher servers to find items that are of interest to the user.

Vertical Blanking Interval (VBI): The period of time between television pictures, which is visible as a black bar when the picture rolls. The VBI contains signals that allow receivers to keep the picture stable and has additional signal capacity that can be used to carry closed captioning information, test, cue and control signals, and other data services.

Vertical Integration: The involvement of cable systems in other links of the video distribution chain, such as programme production and supply.

Vertical Marketing: **(1)** Focusing resources on carefully selected industry groups. **(2)** Offers designed and marketed to appeal to a specific industry group, such as: financial which contains banks, mutual funds and insurance companies.

VHF Drop-Ins: Full power VHF TV stations that may be squeezed into locations that do not comply with the FCC's spacing requirements.

Via Net Loss (VNL): The lowest loss in decibel (dB) at which a trunk facility can be operated considering limitations of echo, crosstalk, noise and singing.

Video Camera: A camera which converts images to electrical signals for recording on magnetic tape or live transmission. Videodisc A record-like device storing a large amount of audio and visual information that can be linked to a computer; one side can store the pictures and sounds for 54,000 separate television screens.

Video Conferencing: Video conferencing is the real-time, usually two-way transmission of voice and images between two or more locations. Today, both voice and video analog signals are digitized by video codices before transmission which can involve wide bandwidths. To conserve bandwidth, some systems employ "freeze frame," where a television screen is only "repainted" every few seconds. Codecs for higher quality full motion video attempt to minimize bandwidth requirements by taking advantage of intervals with relatively little motion (which require smaller bandwidths), and by trading off smooth motion tracking and picture resolution.

Video Description: An audio narration for television viewers who are blind or visually disabled, which consists of verbal descriptions of key visual elements in a television programme, such as settings and actions not reflected in dialog. Narrations are inserted into the programme's natural pauses, and are typically provided through the Secondary Audio Programming channel.

Video Dial Tone (VDT): Video Dial Tone (VDT) is the visual counterpart to basic exchange service audio dial tone whereby video information is switched over a public network. As with audio dial tone, VDT can be used to connect one or more locations for the transmission and exchange of visual and auditory information.

Video Display: Presentation of the TV signal can be as simple as using a 19" TV receiver or as elaborate as large screen projection costing $200,000. The ideal lies somewhere in between. Analyze the room, physical layout, anticipated audience size, and AV support staff. In general, the larger the screen, the better. Projected images produce greater psychological impact, and help to dispel a viewer's feeling that he or she is watching TV. A general rule of thumb that has been suggested concerning minimum screen size is to figure no more than one viewer per diagonal inch.

Video Teleconference: A meeting involving at least one uplink and a number of downlinks at different locations. Electronic voice and video communication between two or more locations. It can be fully interactive voice and video or two-way voice and oneway video. It includes full-motion, compressed, and freeze-frame video.

Video: A term pertaining to the bandwidth and spectrum of the signal which results from television scanning and which is used to reproduce a picture.

Videoconferencing: Two-way telecommunications service with live transmission of pictures and speech of conference participants transmitted between two or more locations.

Video-on-demand: A technology that allows individuals to retrieve, via a television set or a computer, video material stored in a remote database when one wants it (i.e., on demand). The material, which can include films, training videos, or any other video information, can be viewed (at any time) by an individual and manipulated with VCR-like controls (i.e., pause, rewind, fast forward). The same material can also be viewed simultaneously by different people in different locations, allowing them to watch the same or different portions of the video at the same time.

Videotape: A plastic, iron oxide-coated tape of various widths from ¼" to 2" for recording and playback of video and audio signals and additional technical code information.

Videotex: The generic term used to refer to a two-way interactive system(s) for the delivery of computer-generated data into the home, usually using the television set as the display device. Some of the more often used specific terms are "viewdata" for telephone-based systems (narrowband interactive systems); "wideband broadcast" or "cabletext" for systems utilizing a full video channel for information transmission; and "wideband two-way teletext" for systems which could be implemented over two-way cable television systems. In addition, hybrids and other transmission technologies, such as satellite, could be used for delivery of videotex services on a national scale.

Videotext: An interactive service connecting a TV set and text or video recorder to a central computer by phone lines or cable TV. The computer provides textual information on demand and transactional services.

Viewdata: Generic term used primarily in the U.S. and Great Britain to describe twoway information retrieval systems based on mainframe computers accessed by dumb or intelligent terminals whose chief characteristic is ease of use.

Virtual banding: **(1)** A means of assigning calls to bands determined by originating and terminating NPAs, rather than by assigned circuits. **(2)** A method of rating calls based on distance sensitive pricing developed for NPA-to-NPA pairs.

Virtual Private Networks (VPN): VPNs are services using public network facilities augmented by network control point and service management system facilities wherein traffic is routed through the public network under computer control in a manner that makes VPN service indistinguishable from dedicated facilities based private networks. Customers can define, change and control network resources with the same or more flexibility as afforded by facilities based private networks.

Virtual Reality (VR): Loosely defined as putting users into a computer-generated environment, rather than merely reacting to images on a display screen. Full immersion VR can include a helmet that senses head movement and changes the view seen through small TV screens mounted in front of each eye along with gloves that allow users to touch objects in the virtual world.

Virtual Space: Refers to a type of videoconference in which each participant is assigned a separate camera and is seen on a separate monitor, large screen or assigned spatial area.

Visual Display Unit (VDU) : A device, such as a television screen, which produces a visible display of data. It is usually equipped with a keyboard to allow communication with a computer. A hard copy of the images produced on the screen may be reproduced using a printer.

Voice Activation: Method in which spoken messages, rather than electrical signals from a telephone keypad, initiate call processing.

Voice Actuated: Equipment activated in response to a voice. A voice-switched microphone is activated by a voice. In voice-switched video cameras are activated by voice to send a picture of the speaker.

Voice Carry Over (VCO): A reduced form of TRS where the person with the hearing disability speaks directly to the other end user. The Communications Assistant then types the response back to the person with the hearing disability. The Communications Assistant does not voice the conversation.

Voice Connecting Arrangement: An access arrangement provided by the telcos to accommodate the connections of non-carrier provided voice terminal equipment to the public switched telephone network.

Voice Frequency (VF): Any of the frequencies in the 300 to 3400 Hz band which must be transmitted to reproduce the voice with reasonable fidelity.

Voice Grade Facility (VGF): Circuit designed to DDD network standards, making it suitable for voice, low-speed data, facsimile or telegraph service.

Voice Grade: (1) An access line suitable for voice, low-speed data, facsimile or telegraph service. (2) A line that generally has a frequency range of about 300 to 3000 Hz.

Voice Mail: An automatic answering service with the ability to record a message. Unlike simple answering machines, Voice mail uses a programmable computer system with options such as temporary call routing, monitoring and reporting, etc.

Voice Recognition: System of sound sensors that translate the tones of the human voice into computer commands to access or accomplish some service.

Voice Response Unit (VRU): Device that accepts a coded request for data, composes a coded response and interprets the coded response into locations of stored vocabulary as output.

Voice Syntheses: Computer generated sounds that simulate the human voice.

Voiceprint: **(1)** Technique for verifying an individual's identity by his or her speech pattern. **(2)** An individually distinctive pattern of certain speech characteristics that can be mapped electromagnetically; the verbal equivalent of a fingerprint.

Voice-Switched Microphone: Microphone that is activated by a sound of sufficient amplitude; generally allows only one person to speak at a time.

Voice-Switched Video: Type of video conference in which the cameras are activated by voice signals to send a picture of a particular person in the group. Not all participants can be seen at any one time in contrast to continuous presence video.

VoIP: Voice over Internet Protocol - telephone calls (voice) bypass the typical public-switched telephone network and transmit voice calls over a private network.

Volatile Memory: A storage medium in which information is destroyed when power is removed from the system.

W

W3: World Wide Web

Wait State: Condition of a central processing unit when all operations are suspended.

Warm Boot: Reloading the operating system or initializing the computer after it has been on, both without turning the computer off.

Wats Access Line (WAL): A line class marked as a WATS line, provided from an equal access end office. The WATS access line provides the same service and features as a normal business line (unless mixed interstate and intrastate usage is prohibited by the state regulatory body), but incurs access charges which are different from those incurred for a normal business line.

Wats Access Line Extension (WALE): A WAL provided to a customer served by an end office which has not been converted to equal access through an end office which has been converted.

Wavelength Division Multiplexing (WDM): WDM is a means of increasing the capacity of fiber-optic data transmission systems through the multiplexing of multiple wavelengths of light. WDM systems support the multiplexing of as many as four wavelengths.

Wavelength Multiplexing: Transmitting individual signals simultaneously by using a different wavelength for each signal.

Wavelength: The length of one complete wave of an alternating or vibrating phenomenon, generally measured from crest to crest or from trough to trough of successive waves.

Web Browser: Also known as browser - software which collects documents on the World Wide Web and displays them on a computer; the two most popular are Internet Explorer and Netscape Navigator.

Web Hosting: Housing, serving and maintaining files for one or more Web sites on computers owned by providers. Companies and individuals can place their Web sites on the Web host's computers, which are linked by high-speed connections to the Internet. Many Internet service providers, such as AOL, offer free, basic Web site hosting for members. More complex Web sites are increasingly being hosted by specialized companies.

Web-enabled: Able to connect to or be used on the Internet. which serves multiple dwelling complexes such as motels, hotels, and apartments. It is, in effect, a miniature cable system.

Whois: An Internet programme which allows users to query a database of people and other Internet entities, such as domains, networks and hosts, kept at the NIC. The information for people shows a person's company name, address, phone number and e-mail address.

Wide Area Information Service (WAIS): A distributed text search system based on a standard (Z39.50) that describes a way for one computer to ask another to do searches for it. It looks at the content of files (not just the titles).

Wide Area Network **(WAN):** Data communications network that extends a LAN outside its geographic area, over common carrier lines, to link other LANs.

Wide Area Telecommunications Service (WATS): A special direct distance dialing (toll) service whereby a subscriber installs a dedicated line arranged for either inward or outward calls (not both) between the customer's premises and a specific geographic area. Monthly charges are based on the size of the area in which the calls are placed, not on the number or length of calls.

Wideban: Facilities or circuits where bandwidths are greater than that required for one voice channel.

Wideband Network: A wideband network is capable of carrying less information than a broadband network, but more than a narrowband network. Services include: video teleconferencing; file transferring and video telephony. Technically, wideband services are those which require between 64,000 and 1.5 million bits or more of information per second.

Wildcards: Special characters such as and ? that can stand in for other characters during text searches in some programmes. The wildcard generally means "match any other characters in this spot," and the ? generally means "match any other character in this spot."

Wink-Start: Wink-Start is a supervisory signal that consists of an off-hook followed by an on-hook signal, exchanged between two switching systems. The wink-start signal is generated by the called switch to indicate to the calling switch that it is ready to receive address signal digits.

Winsock: A Windows subroutine library that provides access to the Internet TCP/IP.

Wipe: Optical effect in which the picture appears to have been wiped from the screen; i.e. from left to right, top to bottom.

Wire Center: Physical structure that houses one or more central office switching systems.

Wireless: Using the radio-frequency spectrum to transmit and receive voice, data and video signals without a physical cable connection.

Wireless Access Protocol (WAP): WAP was jointly developed in 1999 in the mainstream of Internet standardisation activities, with the broad support of many vendors. It provides the basis for a whole host of new wireless information applications by offering a gateway between the Internet and mobile telephones. If an application can be put on the Internet, it can be made available to mobile terminal users through WAP.

Wireless Cable/Multipoint Distribution Service: Multipoint Distribution Service (MDS) is defined as a medium of mass communications. It may be licensed as a common carrier where non-affiliated programmers, usually pursuant to a tariff on file with FCC, lease time from the MDS licensee to "air" its programming. Alternatively, a licensee may choose to operate as a non-common carrier and programme its own facility of lease transmission time to an affiliated programmer without the requirement of filing a tariff.

Wireless Cable: Uses microwave frequencies to transmit programming to a small antenna at subscriber homes.

Wireless Communication: The transmission of information signals without a physical connection, through technologies such as cordless telephones, cellular telephones or microwaves.

Wireless Internet: Radio-frequency services that provide access to e-mail and the Internet.

Word Processor: A computer-based typing and text-editing system.

Work Area: In a premises distribution system, a work area is an area containing stations and the connections between those stations and their telecommunications (information) outlets.

World Wide Web (WWW): The web of systems and the data in them that is the Internet. Presents information in a user friendly hypertext format. WWW displays pages of information, with links to other pages. Mosaic is the programme that really makes Web materials come alive. Different systems display the links differently, by highlighting the link items or by putting a code after the item. Others put the link in boldface or in color.

Write Once Read Many (WORM): A type of permanent optical storage which allows the user to record information on a blank optical storage disc. Information may be added until the disc is full, but not erased or changed.

Wrap: The end of a programme or production sequence, as in, "That's a wrap."

Wraparound: Local activities prior to, in the midst of, or following a teleconference to focus the content toward outcomes and ideas which can directly assist the participants.